The Munich Glyptothek

The Munich Glyptothek

Greek and Roman Sculpture

A brief guide by Dieter Ohly
with 29 text figures and 48 plates

Verlag C.H.Beck München

The *Cafeteria* in Room VIII offers rest and refreshments.

For *times of opening* see separate sheet enclosed.

Antikensammlungen in the Königsplatz: a ticket purchased at the Glyptothek entitles the holder to visit the Antikensammlungen on the same day at a reduced rate. The Antikensammlungen include the collections of Greek vases and terracottas and Greek and Etruscan goldwork and bronzes.

Offices of the Glyptothek and Antikensammlungen: Karolinenplatz 4, Munich 2 (telephone 28 30 46 / 28 30 47).

Verein der Freunde und Förderer der Glyptothek und der Antikensammlungen, München e. V.: München 2, Wittelsbacher Platz 2 (Siemens AG, Büro der Leitung).

Translated by Helen Hughes-Brock.

ISBN 3 406 03321 0

© C.H. Beck'sche Verlagsbuchhandlung (Oscar Beck) Munich 1974. Printed by C.H. Beck'sche Buchdruckerei, Nördlingen. Layout: Jürgen Fischer. Plates: Brend'amour, Simhart & Co., Munich. Printed in Germany.

CONTENTS

THE ENTRANCE HALL

The *ground-plan of the Glyptothek* (fig. 2, p. 14; also displayed near the entrance to Room I) shows the arrangement of the thirteen exhibition rooms surrounding the quadrangular Inner Court. The visitor is recommended to tour them in their numerical order. The rooms have been given names as follows, after the works exhibited in them.

I Room of the Archaic Kouroi
II Room of the Faun
III Room of Diomede
IV Room of the Grave Relief of Mnesarete
V Room of Eirene
VI Room of the Huntsman Relief

VII Room of the West Pediment of the Aegina Temple
VIII Room of the Sphinx
IX Room of the East Pediment of the Aegina Temple

X Room of the Alexander
XI Room of Roman Portraits
XII Room of Apollo
XIII Room of the Boy with the Goose

Plate	What is where
4–5 7–8	Room I. Portrait of Homer (Roman copy); early Greek kouroi (i.e., statues of youths); Greek votive reliefs; architectural elements from Greek temples
9, 32 48	Room II. Large statue of a Satyr (the "Barberini Faun"); head of Medusa (the "Medusa Rondanini", Roman copy); a Greek votive relief
6, 10 14, 16	Room III. Greek statues (5th century B. C., mostly Roman copies and adaptations): statue of Diomede, statue of a boy, bronze head of a youth, head of Athene
18–19	Room IV. Greek grave monuments (4th century B. C.): grave relief of Mnesarete, gravestone in form of a lekythos (oil-flask) with relief decoration
11–13 15, 17	Room V. Greek statues (4th century B. C., mostly Roman copies and adaptations): Eirene (Peace), athlete, kneeling youth, head of a woman, head of Aphrodite

1. The Greek world and Rome

The Greek world: Peloponnese, Central Greece, North Greece, Aegean islands and Crete; coast of Asia Minor (East Greece); colonies founded between the 8th and 6th centuries B. C. in southern Italy and Sicily (Magna Graecia)
Rome: Dominance in southern Italy and Sicily from 3rd century B. C. – Expansion of Roman power in Asia Minor from 2nd century B. C. – Old Greece becomes a Roman province 27 B. C.

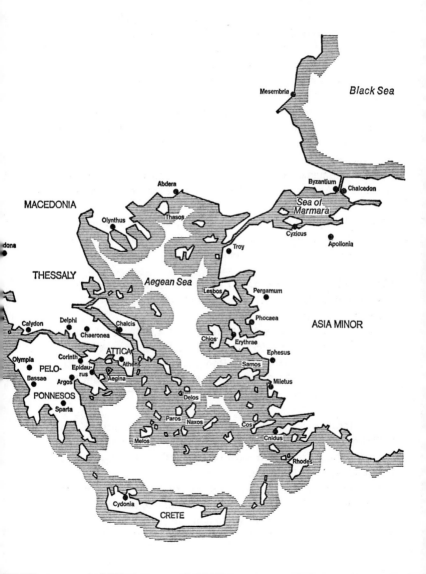

Room VI. Greek grave monuments (5th–4th century B. C.): reliefs *Plate*
of a huntsman and of a woman   *20–21*
Room VII. West pediment group from the Aegina temple, central   *22–24*
akroterion from the temple (ca. 500 B. C.)   *28–29*
Room VIII. Sphinx from the roof of the Aegina temple; crowning
akroterion (ca. 500 B. C.)
Room IX. East pediment group from the Aegina temple; head of a   *25–27*
sphinx (see cover) from temple roof (ca. 480 B. C.)
Room X. Greek statues and grave reliefs (4th century B. C. to   *30–31*
2nd century A. D.): statue of Alexander (the "Alexander Rondanini"); portrait of Demosthenes, head of a goddess (Roman copies); grave relief of Hiras
Room XI. Roman portraits and reliefs, Roman mosaic (1st cent-   *33–45*
ury B. C. to 4th century A. D.): portrait busts and statues; large
relief monument with wedding of Poseidon; relief sarcophagi;
large mosaic from Sentinum
Room XII. Roman copies and adaptations of Greek statues: colossal statue of Apollo ("Apollo Barberini"). – Statue of the Emperor
Domitian
Room XIII. Roman copies and adaptations of Greek statues: Boy   *46–47*
with the Goose, Drunken Old Woman, head of a Satyr. – Roman
reliefs: sarcophagi and relief plaques

The Collection of King Ludwig I of Bavaria is the source of the
greater part of the Glyptothek's present collection. Works from
it are listed below room by room:
Room I: 2, 4–9. Room II: 1–2, 4, 6. Room III: 1–4, 7–10, 13–15. Room
V: 1–6, 8–9, 12–15, 17. Room VI: 9. Room VII: 1–6. Room VIII: 1–4.
Room IX: 1–4, Cases A and B. Room X: 1–2, 3, 9–10. Room XI:
1–4, 6–14, 16–19, 21–27, 30–40, 42–47, 49–53, 55–64, 67. Room XII:
1–3, 5–7 and floor mosaic. Room XIII: 1, 4–13. Inner Court: portrait
of Hadrian.
In 1923 through the decision of Crown Prince Rupprecht this
collection was made over to the Wittelsbacher Ausgleichfonds
so that it should remain in Bavaria and continue to play the part
King Ludwig intended for it.
Donations and bequests. – Auguste Herzogin von Leuchtenberg
(donation 1826): Roman mosaic from Sentinum, Room XI: 42. –
Johann Martin von Wagner (donation 1858): Roman relief with
rustic scene, Room XIII: 13. – Paul Arndt (donation 1892): por-

trait of Homer, Room I: 3. – Franz von Lenbach (donation 1897):
head of Herakles, Room XII: 4. – Friedrich Wilhelm Freiherr von
Bissing (donations 1900 and 1910): grave relief of Mnesarete,
Room IV: 1 and gladiator relief, Room XI: 41. – Edward Perry
Warren (donation 1907): banquet relief, Room VI: 12. – Anna von
Lotzbeck (bequest 1917): Roman head of boy, Room XI: 20. –
Bayerischer Verein der Kunstfreunde (donation 1939): statue of
boy, Room III: 5; head of Aphrodite, Room V: 10; grave lekythos
with man and wife, Room IV: 10; grave relief with lady and maid,
Room VI: 4. – Heinz Herzer (donation 1971): head of a Roman,
Room XI: 5

Inscriptions in the Entrance Hall

The visitor will notice the Latin inscriptions over the main doorway, the door to the Inner Court and the entrances to Rooms I
and XIII (whose original framework of pilasters, entablature and
pediment has now been restored). From them we learn of the
beginning and end of the building's construction, of the royal
founder who conceived and realised the idea of establishing this
museum, of the architect who built it and finally of the painter
commissioned with the decoration of the old reception rooms.
Over the main entrance we read "Begun 1816, completed 1830".
Over the Inner Court door: "Ludwig I King of Bavaria founded
this Museum and dedicated it as a worthy home for the monuments of ancient sculpture which he collected from everywhere".
Over the doorway of Room I: "At the King's command Leo
Klenze, Knight, supervised the construction and decoration of
this building". Over the door to Room XIII: "At the King's com-
mand Peter Cornelius, Knight, decorated the domes with paint-
ings".
The Latin text of the inscriptions reads as follows: INCHOATUM
MDCCCXVI. PERFECTUM MDCCCXXX (over main entrance). –
LUDOVICUS I BAVARIAE REX VETERUM SCULPTURAE
MONUMENTIS QUAE IPSE UNDIQUE CONGESSERAT DE-
CORE COLLOCANDIS HOC MUSEUM CONDIDIT ATQUE
DICAVIT (over Inner Court door). – REGIS IUSSU AEDIFICIO
EXSTRUENDO ET DECORANDO PRAEFUIT LEO KLENZE
EQUES (over entrance to Room I). – REGIS IUSSU CAMERAS
PICTURIS EXORNAVIT PETRUS CORNELIUS EQUES (over
entrance to Room XIII).

The Rooms as they are today

One has but to consider the ground-plan of the Glyptothek (fig. 2)
to realise what a genius its architect was. And how much more
one senses it as one walks through his galleries, denuded though
they now are through war and its consequences, of the quite
exceptional magnificence in which he clothed them. Only the bare   *Pl. 3*
structure of the building now remains, either intact or restored,
and the brickwork of the walls, vaulting and domes has been
lightly whitewashed over. Here, the walls were once covered with
imitation marble panels in gleaming coloured stucco, and there   *Pl. 2*
were brightly painted plaster cornices; variously shaped coffers
of the ceiling were filled with rosettes, stars, ornamental motifs
and figure-scenes. On the upper walls and vaulted ceilings and
over the doorways white stucco reliefs, highlighted in rich gold
and brilliant colours, rang the changes on arabesques, figure-
groups and symbolic, allegorical and decorative motifs. Three
halls (Rooms VII, VIII, IX) had paintings on the ceiling and upper
walls. These were originally reception rooms, containing no
sculpture, where the royal court enjoyed parties by torchlight on
evening visits to the museum. Here too, instead of today's plain
limestone paving, were shining floors of coloured marble.

The great buildings of ancient Rome still move us to amazement
and admiration, though they have lost their original marble or
plaster coverings, and in the same way one is still moved by the
grandeur of Klenze's halls, which were, indeed, inspired by Roman antecedents. We pass through rooms of varying size and
shape – square and oblong rooms, one very long, lower-lying
room on the east side (Room XI), the Entrance Hall with its considerably higher ceiling. The corner rooms on the south side are
round (II and XII), while between them and the Entrance Hall two
rooms (I and XIII) combine square with half-moon shape. The
sequence of rooms in the front of the building, on the Königsplatz, is executed with a particularly striking sense of form and
flexibility (Entrance Hall with Rooms I–II and XIII–XII).

The wall surface is varied with protruding and receding elements,
with niches of various shapes and sizes, with heavy wall-piers or
pilasters, narrow ribbing and framed fields. The entablature runs
all the way around, often broken forward, and above it rises the
vaulting – lofty cupolas in the two round rooms (II and XII), half-
cupolas in the apses of Rooms I and XIII, flat domes on penden-

tives, cross-groined and tunnel vaults in the others. Wide and narrow ribbons of vaulting, which effect the junction with the walls, bound and frame the vaults. And everywhere there are coffers – rectangular as a rule, but sometimes diamond-shaped – which cover the domes and half-domes in diminishing size (Rooms I–II and XIII–XII) or decorate the wide ribbons of vaulting. The doorways between the rooms are mostly square-headed with a straight lintel but some are crowned with a pediment or open into a semi-circular arch above. The round rooms of the south side (II, XII) receive daylight through lanterns in the top of the cupolas, and the corner rooms on the north (VI, X) have triple windows reaching to the floor – the only outer windows in the whole building. All the other rooms received light on the court-yard side through "lunettes" – high-placed, half-moon-shaped windows with a rectangular opening beneath. In the old exhibition galleries (I, III, V, XI, XIII) and in the former great reception rooms (VII, IX) the walls were blank and the only light – not enough – came through the lunettes. It is certain, however, that the architect envisaged windows here originally, for in Rooms I and XIII there were found, beneath the ruined plaster, tall windows divided in three by pillars and reaching from the sill beneath the lunettes to a low parapet wall. But they had been walled up again before the building was finished. With the new windows, which are in two parts and reach down to the floor, Klenze's original plan has been executed in rather different form.

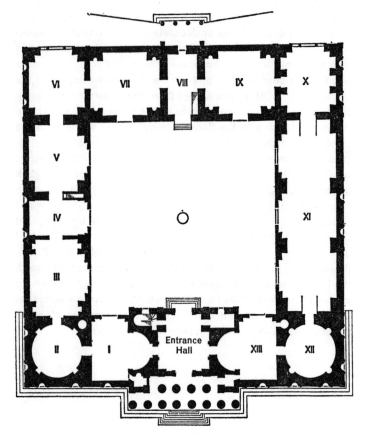

2. Glyptothek

TOUR OF THE EXHIBITS

The works from the Greek and Roman world (see map fig. 1, pp. 8f.) exhibited in Rooms I to XIII span a millennium. The oldest Greek sculptures go back to the sixth century B. C.; the latest Roman Imperial works belong to the fourth century A. D. But the earliest Greek sculpture is the ancestor of the late Roman, for though it underwent many transformations and the centre of gravity shifted, the history of ancient Greek and Roman art is a unity, the first great age of the art of Europe. It was the Greeks who first discovered the organic unity of body and soul and who learnt to portray it as we see it, in its first morning bloom, in the form and countenance of the Kouros of Tenea. It is the fundamental principle of their art. They worked it out, deepened it, developed it to the point of decadence – and we see it still, though changed over the centuries and given new meaning, implicit in the portraits of the Romans.

Rome as conqueror of Greece felt herself to be the heir of Greek art. At the moment when Greek culture seemed on the point of collapse, Rome looked back to the great achievements of the Greeks in the past, turned to them with passionate interest and devoted herself to them thenceforward. She preserved and copied Greek masterpieces and made Greek art available to herself and to posterity, while at the same time giving new impulses and directions for artistic creation.

I ROOM OF THE ARCHAIC KOUROI

As one enters Room I, one's eye is met first of all by the massive back view of the *Kouros* from Attica (1)* in weathered reddish- *Pl. 7* brown marble and the slender-limbed *"Kouros of Tenea"*, whose *Pl. 5* marble still gleams in its pristine whiteness. But one's gaze is at once carried onward into Room II, in the middle of which stands the colossal Satyr known as the "Barberini Faun". In these works, *Pl. 9* which are among the most significant in Greek art, we have before our eyes two epochs of Greek sculpture, its early "archaic" period and its advanced "baroque" stage. The Faun is the plastic expression of powerful, surging, self-liberating movement; here in Room I we have living forms captured forever in an extreme of tensed self-control.

   *Translator's note – The Greek word "kouros", which simply means "youth", has become the standard name for these early Greek statues of young men. In the past they were often, but mistakenly, called "Apollos".

Pls.5,7 The two archaic youths (1, 2) set the tone of the first Room.
They are among the very few statues of this kind to survive
completely preserved and the kouros from Tenea in the neigh-
bourhood of Corinth (2) is so far unique in the art of that
district.

"Early Greek kouroi – what a great, festive, liberating, cheering
word resounds to us from them across the centuries. A pure,
strong sound, which invigorates and refreshes. He who has once
made it his own remains forever moved by it, fired by it, trans-
formed.

This word appears often altered, renewed, transfigured, and
yet for a century and a half it remains the same; from the middle
of the seventh century to the early years of the fifth Greek shrines
and cemeteries were adorned with these statues of young men
of a uniform pose and character: naked, standing upright with
left leg forward and arms hangig down ... the body directed
straight forward with no contrary movement, outwardly motion-
less but filled with the strongest inner excitement, even the head
without turning or inclination but scintillating with shining
countenance and brilliant glance – figures of unending life, of
faultless beauty and utility ... suffused with the spirit's morning
freshness, divine in the Greek, and in every sense." In such
words did Ernst Buschor praise these early kouroi.

Originally the kouroi would have stood in a cemetery, the foot-
plinths being embedded in bases. (Few such bases now survive.) On the base was written the name of the dead man, for
whom the statue served as an idealised substitute. The name
might be repeated in conjunction with a funerary poem (an epigram) and the sculptor's name might appear too. Two Attic epi-
grams may serve as examples. The first is on the base of a kouros
(now in Athens) found not far from ours and of about the same
date. Both are addressed to the passer-by.

"Stop and lament at the tomb of Kroisos, who died one day fighting in the front ranks, slain by violent Ares."

"As you look on the tomb of departed Kleoitas, son of Mene-
saichmos, mourn, for he was beautiful and is dead." (Grave
pillar with the dead man depicted in relief or painting.)

Pl. 5 The marble surface of the Tenea kouros (2) is in an excellent state
of preservation, so that we can observe the still somewhat naive
chiselwork of the early sculptor. But the colours which must once

have adorned it have now entirely faded. (All ancient marble sculptures were painted, but only seldom do traces remain.) The hair, the fillets round the head, the eye with iris and pupil and the lips of the kouroi were picked out in bright colours, while the pubic hair was indicated by painting alone.

The *head (4)*, perhaps from a sphinx, was for some unknown reason left unfinished. The suclptor had got quite far with the right side of the head, while the left was still no more than roughly blocked out. Yet this incomplete work shines from within with life. "No portion of a figure's surface can be created except from the inmost core outwards."

In the gaily elegant dancing maidens on the fine *votive relief from Paros (5)* we may perhaps recognise Aphrodite's charming companions the Graces or "lovely ones" – Aglaia, Euphrosyne and Thalia. Two are seen in profile, the third full face in a severe composition characteristic of early Greek figure-groups.

It is no accident that the *portrait of Homer (3)* is placed in Room I *Pl. 4* at the starting-point of the visitor's tour. For the "Sovereign Founder" of the Hellenic world, who first gave form to the myths of god and man, was the source to whom Greek art und poetry turned again and again for inspiration. The portrait goes back to an idealised 5th-century statue which showed the poet striding and perhaps playing the lyre. The head alone survives in a number of copies and the Munich example can be ranked as the finest. He is shown, as tradition made him, blind, but his sightless face reflects the vision of the seer.

Architectural elements: – The *ornamental moulding from the Erechtheum (8)* once crowned the wall of that temple on the Athens *Pl. 8* Acropolis. It ist a magnificent piece of chiselling, almost as fine and sharp as metalwork. The bottom row is a frieze of palmette and lotus springing from spiral tendrils. Above this, bordered by narrow rows of "bead and reel", is a row of "egg and dart" and at the top a row of "leaf and dart" or "Lesbian pattern".

Also from the Athens Acropolis comes the *palmette (7)* from the roof of the Parthenon. The roof was once covered entirely with marble tiles, and palmette antefixes like this one stood in a continuous row along the long side of the building, serving as a decorative termination of the cover-tiles. (Compare the corresponding marble antefixes from the roof of the Aegina temple, Room VIII: 2 and fig. 15.) – The roof of the temple of Apollo at Bassae in Arcadia (in the Peloponnesos) was also covered entirely with marble. The fragment with a *palmette frieze (9)* belonged to the slanting edge (sima) of the roof above the pediments (cf. roof of Aegina temple, fig. 15).

Glass Case: The Corinthian craftsman, who made the bronze statuette of *Zeus* (solid cast; 530/520 B. C.) with its developed modelling and fine engraved detail must have been an artist of the first rank. The statuette was acquired in 1972 with the help of the "Verein der Freunde und Förderer der Glyptothek und Antikensammlungen".

The bearded god, with long hair and piercing glance, strides forward like a javelin-thrower, poising his wedge-tipped thunderbolt; the other, backward-pointing wedge of this weapon has changed into a coil, to uncoil again in a snaky lightning flash. In his left hand Zeus holds a second bolt, both wedges still closed, in readiness for further thunderstorms.

This unusual figure combines mastery of form with such intense vitality that, though only 16.7 cm high, it holds its own with the marble youths near by. Perhaps it represents "Zeus of Lykaion" (Wolf Mountain) who, as wheather god and rain-maker, enjoyed great honour in Arcadia (Peloponnesos), and at whose festival athletic contests were held.

II ROOM OF THE FAUN

1 The "Barberini Faun", a great sleeping Satyr in Greek "baroque" style, named after the Palazzo Barberini, where it was
   housed when first discovered. Ca. 220 B. C. (Plate 9)
2 Head of Medusa, so-called "Medusa Rondanini" (from Palazzo Rondanini in Rome). Copy of a work by Pheidias, ca.
   440 B. C. (Plate 48)
3 Votive relief showing a sacrifice at a rustic shrine, ca. 200
   B. C. (Plate 32)
4 Small "hekateion" or cult-pillar of the household goddess
   Hecate showing her in triple form with three Graces dancing
   round. Attica, 3rd century B. C.
5 Votive relief of two figures of Pan with pine tree and altar
   between them. Above, a small hekateion and Nymphs dancing in a ring. Attica, 2nd century A. D.
6 Fragment of large votive relief with god or hero seated in a
   rocky landscape, ca. 180 B. C.

The master of the *Satyr (1)*, a veritable Greek Michelangelo, ranks *Pl. 9*
among the greatest sculptors in European art. He may have been
an Athenian. His colossal statue must originally have stood
in the open as a votive offering at a sanctuary of Dionysus, the
god to whose woodland retinue the Satyrs belonged. It was
brought to light in Rome in the reign of Pope Urban VIII (Maffeo
Barberini, 1623–1644) during the building of fortifications in the
ruins of the Emperor Hadrian's Mausoleum (Castel Sant'
Angelo). Presumably the Satyr had been stolen from Greece
and set up somewhere in the neighbouring Roman gardens.
The work has excited the greatest admiration since the day it
was found. Composition and modelling are masterly. The Satyr,
a wild creature with a horse's tail, lies dreaming enraptured in a
drunken slumber, leaning against a rock which is covered with a
panther skin. "One seems to hear his heavy breathing, to see how
the wine has made his veins swell, how his quickened pulse throbs".
An uncouth face, tousled hair with a wreath of ivy leaves and berries
entwined in it, the brows knit together, the mouth half open. His left
arm hung limp, the right is still flung back as when sleep first over-
came him. The artist, "one of the greatest in antiquity, has captured

in this dreamer the surging of natural, supra-personal existence, has portrayed exactly the primeval life of the world of Dionysus".

Attacks on the figure began in Roman times with the boring of a raw hole for a fountain pipe and the reworking of the rock on the spectators' right. After its discovery the back of the marble block was planed off to fit a base and the rock was again reworked. (The original surface of the rock survives only at the back on the left side.) Then the missing parts of the figure were restored in plaster (by Giuseppe Giorgetti and Lorenzo Ottone) though without damage to the original. Finally in the late 18th century Vicenzo Pacetti chiselled down the old surface of the breaks on the legs in order to accommodate his marble restorations. The stylistically incongruous right leg is his work.

Pl. 32   The beautiful *votive relief (3)* known as the "Munich Votive Relief" shows an enchanting scene in a sanctuary shaded by a great plane tree. A solemn ritual is being enacted in the heavy, fragrant stillness of summer. From the branches of the plane tree a cloth is stretched across as backdrop to shield the god and goddess. The lord of the shrine – most likely a god of healing, perhaps Asklepios – sits on a throne adorned with winged, goat-horned lions. In front of him leaning on a pillar stands his wife. Each holds a long sceptre. Beside the tree (which has a ribbon tied round it) there is an old-fashioned image of a god and goddess atop a tall pillar. The middle of the scene is occupied by the altar, to which a family has come to make offerings – the father dipping into the basket of offerings, the son and the mother. A small child has brought a second, covered basket. Other members of the party follow behind – little children and two women, one of whom is wearing a sunhat.

The *hekateion (4)* has a hole on the top for a metal pin which must have held an offering-bowl. These little cult pillars of Hecate were often set up as guardians at the doors of houses. At the entrance to the Acropolis of Athens Hecate was worshipped in conjunction with the Graces.

Large *votive relief (6)*, fragment with edge preserved on the right side. A god or hero of the hunt sits on a ledge in a rocky landscape by the knotty trunk of a large tree. To the right in a hollow of the rock we see a hunting-hound and on the summit a pillar, on which apparently hangs a slain animal. The pillar must have marked the ancient cult place in the rustic sanctuary.

The *head of Medusa (2)* from the Palazzo Rondanini in Rome was   *Pl. 48*
repeatedly admired by Goethe when he lodged across from that
palace. He speaks of this "work of art which belongs to a primeval
age of myth", of this "marvellous work expressing a state between
death and life", of the "face of exalted beauty", in which the
mouth in particular has an "indescribable and inimitable nobility".
The "Medusa Rondanini" is a copy, the finest of six surviving
from Roman Imperial times, of the Gorgon-head on the shield of
Athene Parthenos, the cult statue which stood in the Parthenon.
This colossal image was fashioned in gold and ivory by the greatest master of the classical period. The uncovered parts such as
face and arms were of ivory, the other surfaces (garments, helmet)
of beaten gold. The enormous round shield, which rested upright
and was over 4 m high, was no doubt of bronze. The middle of
it was occupied by the Gorgon's face, a terrifying winged mask
with a border of writhing serpents. The rest of the shield bore
mythical scenes in relief which were copied, like the Medusa,
to the same scale.

III ROOM OF DIOMEDE

We now come to the west side of the building, where there is a series of four rooms (Rooms III–VI) with *Greek sculpture of the classical period*, i. e. the 5th and 4th centuries B. C. Rooms III and V contain statues in the round, mostly in copies made during the time of Roman rule over Greece (see map, fig. 1).

The statues made by the great "classical" masters – bronze or marble works set up in sanctuaries or state market-places – have with few exceptions perished. That many of them are nonetheless known to us is due to the brisk activity of the copyists of later antiquity, especially of the Roman Imperial period. Without these copies we should have but scant knowledge of the attainments of most of the leading sculptors of the 5th and 4th centuries – almost nothing but literary references and brief descriptions by

ancient authors, from which it would be impossible to picture in
the mind's eye what the works really looked like. We should know
nothing of the appearance of a single one of the many statues made
in the 5th-century by the famous Polyclitus or by Phidias of Athens,
we could scarcely picture to ourselves the work of Phidias' pupil
Alcamenes, and the work of Cresilas and other contemporary
artists would be a closed book. But the copies afford us a priceless
glimpse of the richness and the development of classical sculpture,
even if only in outline, so to speak, and with varying degrees of
fidelity. Not only were the statues themselves copied, their much-
admired style also furnished inspiration for all sorts of modula-
tions and free adaptations. (The originals cannot often be attributed without dispute, if indeed at all, to this or that known sculptor.)
The naked male form was the central theme of Greek art. We met
it in the archaic grave statues in Room I (I: 1 and 2) and now we   *Pls. 5,7*
meet it again in the statue of Diomede (1) which gives this Room   *Pl. 6*
its name, in the two torsos from statues of Apollo (3, 4) and in
the large statue of a bearded god or hero (2). The first Apollo
(3; after an original dated ca. 460 B. C.) is separated from the
great 6th-century Attic kouros by about two generations. The
second Apollo (4; from original ca. 420), the Diomede (1; from
original ca. 430) and the bearded figure (2; from original ca. 440)
were made between two and four decades after that. Between the
6th- and 5th-century statues lies, one may think, a world of difference – and yet in their fulness of life and spirit both are unalter-
ably Greek and very much brothers from one family.

The beginning of the 5th century sees a rejection of the exagger-
ated constraint and self-containment of archaic sculpture. This is
a change of the greatest consequence. It is as if the laws which
had hitherto governed plastic form were revoked and the sculp-
tured figure set free from bonds. The always inherent "inner
excitement" (as Buschor terms it) is loosed and liberated from
the restraint of outward motionlessness. Such a reordering of
artistic principle brought with it an unprecedented deepening of
expression. (We begin to see this already in the sculptures from
the Aegina temple pediments, pp. 63f.) It also spelt the end of
the spontaneous primeval exuberance which the archaic youths
radiate. The figure is no longer content, as the archaic was, to
rest in self-sufficiency. Face and form are filled with a new
seriousness. In place of symmetrical structure and gently upward-

pointing verticality, we see a whole new world of complex, inter-weaving movements – the torso doubles over, stretches and twists, shoulders rise or droop, the weight on the hips shifts, the limbs relax, the head turns and inclines freely. Above all there is a consciousness of a "centre of gravity", both physical and spirit-ual, which determines the stance of a figure as if from within its own being. This results in a delicate balance between the urge for free movement and the sense of the body's mass. Note in statue 2, for example, the play between the "free" leg and the leg which bears the weight. This rhythmic "dialogue" of weight and freedom is carried on through the whole of a figure, even to the pose of the head.

Torso of Apollo (3). How this statue originally looked can be seen from a sketch (fig. 4) based on better preserved copies. The left hand, slightly raised, held bow and arrow, the lowered right hand a sprig of laurel, Apollo's sacred plant. From the distribution of the weight the figure's pose is clear even from the mere torso. This is probably a late work of the Aeginetan sculptor Onatas, who was already working in the first decades of the 5th century. It was frequently copied in later antiquity.

The second _Apollo (4)_ is one of the chief works of the great Polyclitus of Argos, who was also the author of a book, the so-called "Canon", on the proportions of the human body. Later ancient writers refer to this famous statue as the "Diadoumenos", i. e. "the man binding his hair" (see sketch fig. 5, partly restored from other copies). It may have stood in the market-place of Athens in the vicinity of the temple of Ares. Compared with the Apollo torso (3) the Diadoumenos is less severe and lighter in its movement; the composition forms a harmonious sweeping curve. There ist more animation, too, in the modelling. The god raises his arms to tie the two ends of ribbon. There is an impressive modern bronze cast of Polyclitus's best known work, the Achilles known as the Spear-bearer (Doryphoros) by the staircase in Munich University.

_Pl. 10_ No. _5_ is a charming _statue of a boy_ resting with his left arm against a pillar, tired after his victory in the games. This can scarcely be after a late work of Polyclitus. More probably it was after a work by a pupil or a close follower.

_Pl. 6_ The _Diomede (1)_ is known in many copies, of which the Glypto-thek's is one of the best. It can be ascribed without hesitation

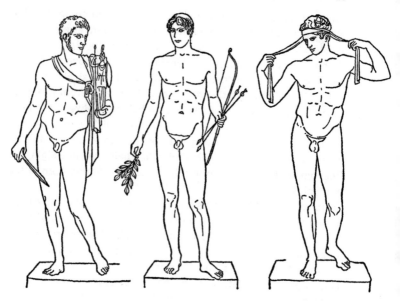

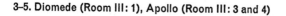

3–5. Diomede (Room III: 1), Apollo (Room III: 3 and 4)

to Cresilas, who came from Kydonia in Crete (destroyed by Aegina in the 6th century but resettled) and worked in Athens in the circle around Phidias. Among his best known pieces was a portrait statue of the Athenian statesman Pericles which stood on the Acropolis. The Diomede was originally set up in Argos. It shows the Greek hero of the Trojan War holding his drawn sword in his right hand, his body turned towards the left with an air of fury and determination (completed sketch fig. 3). In his slightly raised left hand he holds the little cult statue of Troy's patron goddess, Athene. This, says tradition, he and Odysseus had stolen together during the Sack of Troy. But as Diomede was carrying it away, Odysseus, wanting the glory to himself, decided to fight him. Diomede is here wheeling around, ready to defend himself. From his violent movement and forbidding glance many have concluded that the figure was part of a group and that the sculptor is here portraying the moment of highest tension between the two adversaries.

The large *statue of a god or hero (2)* turning towards the left probably belonged to a group too. The stump-shaped support was added by the copyist. The raised left hand no doubt held some identifying attribute. Traces on the base and upper thigh show that the lowered right hand held a pair of lances.

Pl. 14 The lovely *bronze head of a boy (7)* is all that is left of a once complete statue. The lips bear traces of gilding and the fillet knotted at the back of the head may once have been decorated with silver inlay. When the work was discovered in the 18th century it was complete, but the body (naked) was subsequently destroyed. Some time later the inlaid eyes were lost. They were silver with garnet pupils. The head is not a copy of any particular Greek work; it is a Roman creation, made at a period which was consciously striving to recover the severe harmony of classical Greek sculpture.

The large *head of Ares (9)*, the dark-glancing god of war, is taken from the cult statue which stood in the Temple of Ares in Athens (see fig. 6, sketch based on a copy in the Louvre). The sculptor was Alcamenes, a pupil of Phidias and himself one of the outstanding masters of the second half of the 5th century. The elaborate decoration of the helmet includes winged griffins, volutes, palmettes and little hounds, while the support for the crest takes the form of a crouching sphinx.

In the *bearded head (10)* we may have another copy from Alcamenes. Taken from a statue of a god (Zeus?) or hero, it once crowned a cult-pillar (herm).

Pl. 16 The large *bust of the goddess Athene (15)* was probably copied (in the 2nd century A. D., as the form of the bust indicates) from a colossal cult statue in Athens by Cresilas. (See fig. 7, a sketch from a copy in the Louvre of the whole statue.) Her helmet, pushed back over her curly hair, was originally furnished with a crest poised on a coiled serpent. It is of the so-called Corinthian type, cutout eye-holes and nose- and cheek-guards. The goddess had inlaid eyes of some coloured material but these are now lost. Around her neck, as a kind of narrow, decorative cloak, she wears her aegis, the mythical weapon with which she safeguards her friends and terrifies her enemies. It has a border of knotted snakes

6–7. Ares (Room III: 9), Athene (Room III: 15)

and an old-fashioned Gorgon-head serves as clasp. "Of all her many statues, none expresses more clearly and purely than this one the Greek poets' conception of Athene as the virgin goddess of thought and knowledge, the friend and protectress of all brave, noble and intelligent men" (Adolf Furtwaengler).

The small *statue of Athene (12)*, preserved in torso only, is an original of considerable liveliness. The upraised right hand must have held an upright lance. The left arm was lowered and a fragment with the remains of a serpent indicates that the aegis was slung over the hand. Like a number of Greek originals once in Italian hands, this little statue was brought from the East by the Venetians. It was formerly in the Palazzo Giustiniani-Recanati in Venice.

1   Grave relief of Mnesarete. Attica, ca. 380 B. C. (Plate 19)
2   Two pantheresses. Attica, ca. 380 B. C.
3   Grave monument of Xenokrateia. Attica, ca. 350 B. C.
4   Statue of mourning maiden from a grave. Attica, ca. 360 B. C.
5   Statue of girl with a dove, from a sanctuary. Attica, ca. 310 B. C.
6   Grave relief of Plangon. Athens, 320/310 B. C.
7   Gravestone of Paramythion with vase in relief. Athens, 370/360 B. C.
8   Grave relief of Demetrios, a soldier at sea. From Panderma near Cyzicus, Sea of Marmara. Ca. 370 B. C.
9   Relief with young athlete gazing at his spear. From a statue base with athletic scenes (right end sawn off in modern times). Attica, ca. 320 B. C.
10 Woman's grave monument in form of a lekythos (oil-flask) with couple clasping hands. Attica, ca. 375 B. C. (Plate 18)
11 Lekythos, grave monument of Philon, a soldier. Attica, ca. 400 B. C.
12 Lekythos with woman showing the dead mother her child. Attica, ca. 390 B. C.

Room IV is the first of two rooms devoted chiefly to *classical grave monuments* from Athens and its environs. (The other is Room VI.)

Pl. 19 The wonderful gravestone of Mnesarete (1), which dominates Room IV, is among the most beautiful of the 4th-century Attic grave monuments which have come down to posterity, while the

Pl. 18 monument in lekythos shape (10) with the relief depicting a man and wife is unique. There is not another like it of equal quality.

Peerless in all Greece in richness and significance, the classical funerary art of Athens was the product of an interval between two periods of legal restriction against extravagance in funerals and grave-cult. It blossomed in the course of the second half of the 5th century and dwindled again after new state intervention towards the end of the 4th.

The most important are the large *relief slabs* made like

Pl. 19 Mnesarete's (1) by leading artists and even by sculptors who normally worked in other fields. (Praxiteles, for example, one of the greatest of the Athenian marble-sculptors of the 4th century, is said to have made funerary monuments.) Side by side with the large relief monuments there are smaller ones of various design, such as Plangon's (6). The field of decoration on the elongated shaft is frequently of quite modest proportions, as on the East Greek gravestone of Demetrios (8). (Cf. drawings of Attic family graves, figs. 12 and 13.)

Xenokrateia's gravestone (3) belongs to a different class. This kind of tall, *flat pillar* with plant ornament only and no figure relief was often erected to mark the centre of a newly-laid out family plot, so that subsequent graves could be grouped around it (fig. 13). Later it might be re-used, as the other types were also, for another member of the family. Conversely a single individual sometimes had more than one monument, e. g. both a plain column and a slab with figure-subjects.

Vase-shaped monuments were often erected as supplementary monuments alongside the chief one or set up symmetrically in pairs along the edge of a family plot. (Hence they are sometimes called "boundary stones". Vessels are also depicted in relief, as on Paramythion's monument, 7). The same is true of the animal figures – panthers (2), lions and hounds (hunting hound, Room VI: 2) or fantastic beings such as Sirens (cf. p. 43), which stood in pairs around the edge of the plot as guardians. There were also figures of mourners placed near the gravestones; such is the little statue of a mourning maiden (4), which, as its pose indicates, was one of a pair. The vase-shaped monuments themselves are usually in the form of either lekythos or loutrophoros and are simply large-scale stone versions of clay pots. The lekythos is the little clay flask for the oil which was used first for anointing the dead body and afterwards on repeated occasions by pious visitors to the grave, who would then anoint the gravestone as the dead person's substitute. The small clay lekythoi were deposited in the grave along with the body or were placed on the steps of the monument. The loutrophoros on the other hand was a special kind of water jug used for a bride's ritual bath before her marriage. If a person died unmarried, a stone loutrophoros might be erected over the grave as a kind of consolation.

Inscriptions, either cut in the stone or painted on (but now faded) gave the dead person's name, frequently coupled with the father's name, place of origin and the names of other family members who are represented.

He or she might also be commemorated in a grave poem or "epigram". (Even quite eminent poets composed these now and then.) Of the painted decoration there is generally nothing left but occasional traces of pigment or corrosion where there was once an ornamental border on the stone, a coloured background to a picture, or decorative motifs and figure-scenes. (See gravestone of Paramythion: 7.)

The *scenes on the grave monuments* are nearly always taken from life on earth, not from the afterlife or the circumstances of death. The dead are shown as they were in life: the dead woman in her easy chair in the company of a young girl (1) or of her maid who holds her trinket-box (Room VI: 4) or of the nurse holding her child (12). To show that they are still united in spirit, the dead person is often clasping hands with a dear one – so the dead wife with her husband (10), the dead son with his father (Room VI: 3). Or we see them in the family circle, like the man and wife with children and grandfather and a female attendant (Room VI: 9) A little girl stands before us with the toy she used to play with at home (6). The youth who loved hunting rests against a rock in the open air with his hound beside him (Room VI: 1). "The grave monuments are affectionate and touching and always portray life. The artist . . . depicted nothing but the person's simple presence, so as to continue its existence and make it permanent." And yet these lifelike and sociable scenes are overshadowed by a kind of restrained melancholy. The portrayal of the departed in the midst of his family cannot but carry with it the recurrent realisation that he is gone forever and that their companionship has passed into the sphere of unreality. The observant beholder can nearly always pick out the dead person from among his companions. He is the one who looks wearied, withdrawn or rapt in contemplation, who seems to be less "there"; and those represented with him in everyday scenes seem moved by suppressed sorrow.

Pl. 19

Grave relief of Mnesarete (1). Mnesarete sits with bowed head on a chair with ornamentally turned legs, her feet resting on a shapely footstool. In her right hand she grasps the hem of her mantle as though about to cover her head. Bevore her stands a young girl with hands clasped. The two are wrapt in profoundest stillness;

Margin plate references:
Pl. 19
Pl. 20
Pl. 18
Pl. 21
Pl. 19

their dialogue is silent and entirely spiritual. Beneath the little pediment we read the dead woman's name: "Mnesarete (daughter) of Sokrates." On the architrave supported by pillars, is inscribed an epigram: "This woman left behind husband and brothers and child, sorrow for her mother and the undying glory of great virtue. Here Mnesarete, who reached the summit of all virtue, is held in Persephone's chamber." This little poem, which twice praises Mnesarete's virtue (her name means "mindful of virtue") also speaks of the House of Hades, where Hades and Persephone dwell and preside over the underworld kingdom to which the dead go on their last journey.

The pair of female *panthers (2)* was discovered together with Mnesarete's relief and must have stood at either side on the corners of the wall of a grave-plot, probably a family plot with several graves and monuments (cf. p. 41 and figs. 12, 13). The mighty figures of these exotic wild animals kept guard over the hallowed ground like watchdogs.

The *grave column of Xenokrateia (3)* terminates in a pattern of curling tendrils and waving foliage with little flowers and a bud strewn among them, all worked in fine relief and once brightly painted. The inscription reads "Xenokrateia daughter of Eukleides from Oie" (a place in Attica). Visible beneath it are two disk-like blossoms, originally picked out in colour. Part of the name "Eukleides" is broken off – presumably her father, who must have died later.

Grave relief of Plangon (6), a little girl whose name meant "doll". She wears a high-belted dress and a festive diadem in her hair. On the wall hang playthings – a little bag for dice or knucklebones and another object, whose purpose is unknown. In her left hand she holds a little bird, in the right a dolly which has awakened the curiosity of the goose standing in front of her. It is in fact a little statue of a goddess of a kind pious Greek children used to play with.

The *grave relief of Paramythion (7)* was once richly painted, as is clear from traces of flaking pigment and corrosion. (Cf. picture displayed near it and see also fig. 8 based on photograph by the Doerner Institute, Munich. The lighter patches now visible on the marble were originally painted.) On the body of the loutrophoros (see p. 30) two figures are represented – Paramythion, apparently drawing her veil, and a man called Pheidiades whose name is cut

8. Gravestone of Paramythion (Room IV: 7)
with reconstruction of the original painting

on the upper edge. The ornament on the vase includes rays,
a maeander, tongues on the shoulder and an S-shaped spiral on
the narrow neck. To the left of the vase hang two rolled-up ribbons
(taeniae), and another being wound through the spiral handle of
the loutrophoros. Two more rolled-up ribbons lie on the ground
with two tube-shaped oil-flasks in front of them, since the body
before burial was not only anointed with oil but also adorned with
ribbons, and the gravestone afterwards was treated in the same
way. The slab has an upper border of leaf pattern and is crowned
with a finial of palmette and spirals.

The East Greek *grave relief (8)* "of Demetrios son of Alexes"
shows him as a soldier fighting on the bridge of a warship. Only
the front third with ram, prow and rail is represented. Underneath
the little relief the words of an epigram have been broken off,
leaving only the beginnings of two words: "Among those who
... as fighters in the front rank ..."

Pl. 18 The noble *lekythos (10)* is a work of incomparably intense and
tender feeling. The dead person is the veiled woman at whom the

man is directing his gaze. She, however, bows her head and looks past him, not grasping the hand he offers. There was a painted band running beneath the neck of the vase. Painting was also used for the borders and the background of the relief and for some of the details, e. g. the walking-stick on which the man leans. (His left hand is wrapped in his mantle.)

V ROOM OF EIRENE

1 Eirene, goddess of Peace, copy of a statue by Cephisidotus (ca. 370 B. C.; Plate 17)
2 Silen with child Dionysus, copy (310/300 B. C.)
3 Statue of an athlete, copy (360/350 B. C.; Plate 13)
4 Torso of kneeling youth, ca. 300 B. C. (Plate 11)
5 Dead son of Niobe, copy (ca. 320 B. C.)
6 Head of Ares. Copy, probably of a statue by Lysippus (ca. 330 B. C.)
7 Head from statue of an athlete? 310/300 B. C.
8 Head from statue of a woman. East Greek, 300/280 B. C. (Plate 15)
9 Aphrodite, free copy after statue by Praxiteles (350/340 B. C.)
10 Head from statue of Aphrodite, 300/290 B. C. (Plate 12)
11 Head of a boy (Eros?), ca. 280 B. C.
12 Two copies of statue of a Satyr by Praxiteles (ca. 320 B. C.)
13 Head of Pan known as "Winckelmann's Faun" (once owned by J. J. Winckelmann). Copy of statue of an athlete (ca. 390 B. C.). Pan's horns modern.
14 Head from statue of a woman. Attic, ca. 310 B. C.
15 Head of a woman (Muse?), copy from a statue (ca. 180 B. C.)
16 Head of a woman. Copy, probably of a statue of Sappho by Silanion (340/330 B. C.)
17 Torso of Artemis, free copy of statue by Praxiteles (360/350 B. C.)

Room V houses for the most part originals and copies of *statues from the 4th century*, the late classical period which developed from the early and mature classical seen in Room III. From the Apollo torsos (III: 3, 4) and the Diomede (III: 1) we come to the athlete in the middle of this room (V: 3), from the head of Ares copied from Alcamenes (III: 9) to a head of the same god copied, probably, from one of the great 4th-century masters, Lysippus (V: 6). The severe physical norm of the 5th century now loosens up and the strict canons of proportion governing face and body are relaxed. The figures seem bathed and transfigured in a silver light in which they look less real, for this is the century which discovered whole new dimensions of the human spirit, the centu-

9. Eirene with the child Ploutos (Room V: 1), personifications of Peace and Plenty

ry of Plato, who confronted earthly existence with the transcendental realm of Ideas where the soul originates and to which it must return. For Plato art is a beautiful illusion or, as he once puts it, a waking dream – a judgment which can be seen to touch on the very heart of the art of his time.

The fluid lines and the pensive, preoccupied expression of the *athlete (3)* bring before our eyes in striking form the new introvertedness of 4th-century feeling. It was made on commission by an unknown artist in honour of a victor in the Games. The young man is shown quite self-absorbed as he sets about his toilet after his victory, letting oil drip into his open left palm from a tiny pot held in his upraised right hand (see completed sketch, fig. 11). *Pl. 13*

The *statue of Eirene (1)* is attested by several copies, this being the best. It was commissioned by the city of Athens as a cult statue to be honoured by annual sacrifices in the market-place in commemoration of the "universal peace" proclaimed by Athens and Sparta. The sculptor was a native son, Cephisodotus. He was *Pl. 17*

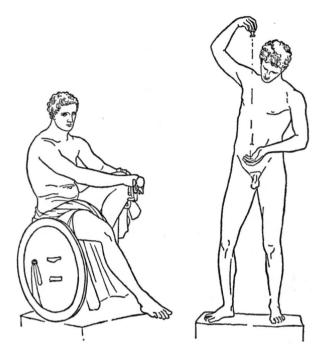

10.–11 Ares (Room V: 6), an athlete (Room V: 3)

probably Praxiteles father. Eirene's right hand held a sceptre, on her left perches a divine child. This little boy is Hades, king of the dead and lord of the underworld, but here seen instead as a little boy and in his other role, that of dispenser of the fruits which spring from beneath the earth. Hence his name Ploutos, "Plenty". Eirene gazes down at him with motherly tenderness, for he personifies the dawning prosperity promised by the conclusion of peace. The little boy stretches his right arm up towards his mother with a loving look. His left hand grasps the horn of plenty (see fig. 9 for an idea of the statue as complete).

In the *Silen (2)* dandling the infant Dionysus we may well have a copy of a work by the Peleponnesian sculptor Lysippus of Sicyon. Although son of Zeus, Dionysus did not grow up among the other gods but in the open air with mountain nymphs. Here the artist has put him in the arms of one of the wild creatures who formed his retinue when he grew up, a goat-tailed old Silen with half-animal ears. The Silen, supporting himself against a tree trunk, rocks and fondles the gay little boy, talking to him, answering his chuckles with a tender, fatherly look. Both wear a garland of leaves and berries of the god's sacred ivy.

The *Ares (6)* too is probably a copy (a fine one, though somewhat weathered) from Lysippus (see fig. 10, a sketch of the complete figure from a copy in the Museo Nazionale delle Terme, Rome). The god was sitting on a rock, his hands clasped round his drawn-up left knee, weary, relaxed and "at ease" (though still grasping his sword). But at the same time he is vibratingly alert, with the watchful, dangerous expression befitting restless War.

From works by the famous Athenian Praxiteles (who made the well-known marble statue in the Olympia Museum of Hermes bringing the infant Dionysus to the Nymphs) we have four copies – two from a statue of a Satyr (12), one from an Aphrodite (9) and the little Artemis (17). The last two, however, are less faithful to their originals.

Statues of a Satyr (12). The Satyr of Praxiteles has come down to us in numerous copies. The headless one is certainly the truer of these two. The other, though complete, fails to capture the youthful sprite's easy grace and we miss the soft lifelike finish (still conveyed by the torso) so much admired in Praxiteles's works. The combination of human beauty and goatish wildness must have lent the statue a peculiar charm. The Satyr has pointed ears and appropriately shaggy hair and wears a panther skin. The trunk he leans upon has been rendered variously by the copyists.

Statue of Aphrodite (9). "The Venus of Praxiteles surpasses all other works of art in the world." In such terms, centuries after its creation, did an unknown writer (Pseudo-Lucian) praise the "Aphrodite of Cnidus". It stood in a narrow chapel in her sanctuary on the peninsula of Cnidus in southern Asia Minor and in later antiquity countless art-lovers made the voyage there solely in order to set eyes on it. "At once breezes of love seemed to waft over us, even from the very precinct... The berry-laden myrtle flourished there in surpassing abundance... cypresses and plane trees as high as the heavens . . . Every tree was entwined with amorous ivy. Spreading vines were hung with thick clusters of grapes... Then we entered the temple. The goddess – a most beautiful work of Parian marble – stands in the middle, full of majesty . . ., gently smiling. All her beauty is revealed, for there is no garment draped about her . . . The temple has a door at each end for the benefit of those who wish to obtain a good view of the goddess from behind, so that no part of her beauty should be left unadmired."

The numerous copies convey but a feeble idea of this celebrated statue. The Glyptothek's copy (9) is no exception, for it reduces to triviality the goddess's sublime and timeless gesture – she was at her bath, with her left hand letting her garment drop over a large water jar and her gaze directed into the distance – by making it look as though she has been taken by surprise and is hastily pulling up the drapery to cover herself. At the time of its creation the Cnidian Aphrodite was revolutionary. Until then the female nude was unknown in large-scale Greek sculpture. Praxiteles was the first to make a cult statue of the goddess of love naked, and indeed he could not have taken this shrewd step in portraying any other woman but her. The naked Aphrodites made after that stood under the spell of the great Athenian's masterpiece.

Pl. 12 The *head of Aphrodite (10)* with her hair tied up above her forehead – a lovely, expressive piece – comes from another famous nude Aphrodite, which again has come down to us in later copies.

The little *Artemis* (17) is a free copy of an Artemis by Praxiteles who held a bow in her lowered left hand, while her right was reaching up into her quiver for an arrow.

The *woman's head (16)*, full of lofty dignity, probably goes back to a statue by Silanion which was later removed to Rome. (It was Silanion who made a statue of Plato during the philosopher's lifetime for the Academy in Athens.)

Pl. 11 *Torso of a kneeling youth (4)* twisting up towards the right in helpless self-defence was part of a group, perhaps from the pediment of a temple. Attested already in the 16th century, in the 17th it was in the possession of the Emperor Rudolph II. A restoration in marble planned in the 19th century was fortunately not carried out.

Dead son of Niobe (5), the finest of the three surviving copies, represents the sprawling corpse of one of the fourteen children of Niobe slain with arrows by Apollo and Artemis to punish their mother's overweening pride in her fertility. (Cf. Roman sarcophagus with slaying of the seven sons and seven daughters, Room

XIII: 6.) These "Niobids" were famous in antiquity and were ascribed to either Scopas or Praxiteles. In the 1st century A. D. the group was in Rome and the many figures repeatedly copied. They were shown loosely disposed in an artificial landscape of rising and falling rocky slopes, Niobe herself (also known from copies) standing on an eminence in the middle with the youngest daughter clinging to her mother's bosom for refuge.

VI ROOM OF THE HUNTSMAN RELIEF

1 Grave relief of youth shown as huntsman. Attica? Ca. 360 B. C. (Plate 21)

2 Hunting hound, from a cemetery. Attica, ca. 360 B. C.

3 Grave relief of Artemon. Attica, ca. 350 B. C.

4 Grave relief with woman and her maid. Attica, ca. 400 B. C. (Plate 20)

5 Grave relief with lyre-player. West Greek, from south Italy, ca. 420 B. C.

6 Head from statue of a little girl, probably from a sanctuary. Attica, ca. 320 B. C.

7 Relief slab with woman mourning. East Greek, from southern Asia Minor, ca. 340 B. C.

8 Grave lekythos (i. e. monument in shape of oil-flask) with three women. Attica, 350/320 B. C.

9 Grave lekythos of Eukoline. Athens, ca. 400 B. C.

10 Fragment of grave relief with Lamprokles. Attica, ca. 360 B. C.

11 Fragment of grave relief with head of mourning girl. Attica, 340/330 B. C.

12 Grave relief with couple at a banquet. East Greek, ca. 320 B. C.

13 Torso from statue of a girl, ca. 300 B. C.

The Greeks buried their dead outside their cities and settlements, frequently along the roads and paths leading out into the country. In the 5th and 4th centuries graves were often grouped together in family plots. A number of such *4th century family cemeteries*, with some of the gravestones still standing, have been discovered outside the Sacred Gate (one of the city gates) of Athens. Each plot was enclosed by retaining walls, above which the monuments within were visible. Figs. 12 and 13 (the diagram in this room) give a view, partly reconstructed, of two neighbouring plots so that one can imagine how this or that one of the monuments displayed in Rooms IV and VI looked in its original setting.

The right-hand plot, with its heavy ashlar wall finished off with a ledge, was constructed along the road outside the Sacred Gate after the death of Koroibos, son of Kleidemos, ca. 370 B. C., on

12. A family grave, Athens, 4th century B. C.

a spot where earlier ancestors had already been buried. His tall plain pillar with palmette finial rises nearly 20 feet above the level of the road (cf. Xenokrateia's monument, Room IV: 3). Beneath Koroibos's name we read the names of a son and a grandson, Kleidemos and another Koroibos, for whom the pillar served in their turn. Close up beside it stands the noble grave relief of Hegeso (now in the National Museum in Athens; it shows her seated, with her maid), probably Koroibos's wife, who had died some 30 years before, ca. 400 B. C. (cf. Mnesarete's relief, Room IV :1 and no. 4 in this room). There is evidence that a second monument was set up in Hegeso's honour next to the relief. This one was a stone lekythos (oil-flask), perhaps with another picture of her (cf. the lekythos with married couple or that with seated woman and female attendant, Room IV: 10, 12). To the right stands the gravestone of Koroibos's brother Kleidemos, who died unmarried ca. 400 B. C. Hence the two-handled loutrophoros on his stone (for explanation see p. 30).

Pls. 19, 20

Pl. 18

The left-hand structure is of polygonal masonry and finished off with tiles. It was built ca. 330 B. C. by one Eubios for his son Bion, who died unmarried. Bion's monument is a column crowned by a loutrophoros. On either side of it stand earlier monuments: to the right the relief of Bion's mother Demetria, shown seated in a chair, surrounded by her sorrowing husband and other relations

13. A family grave, Athens, 4th century B. C.

(360/350), to the left that of Euphrosyne (350/340), the sister of
Bion's father. She appears in the little picture seated in the presence of her brother and Bion, then a young boy. Both this cemetery and Koroibos's may well have contained other monuments
which have since disappeared.

Pl. 21   The *grave relief with a huntsman (1)* of reddish pitted stone gives
its name to Room VI. On it the dead young man is portrayed
holding in his right hand the throwing-stick he used for catching
hares. He looks tired and has thrown his cloak over a rock and is
sitting upon it. His hound looks up at him shyly.

The superb figure of a *dog (2)* on the scent of game did not actually come from the grave of the "huntsman". But it is quite possible
that there was a similar dog there, or even a symmetrically placed
pair (cf. p. 30 for animal figures in cemeteries).

On *Artemon's relief (3)* we see the dead man, who died in middle
age, clasping hands with an older man, probably his father, who
has a walking-stick. The picture is framed by pillars supporting
a horizontal roof and on the centre of the roof atop a small base
stands a Siren with wings outspread. Two sphinxes crouch outside.
Sirens recur constantly on Greek grave monuments. Sometimes
they were sculpted as figures perching on cemetery walls. They
were friendly beings, half bird, half woman, who inhabited the next
world and charmed the dead with their music. They are depicted

playing the lyre to the dead or bewailing their fate, like the Siren on Artemon's monument who beats her breast and tears her hair.

Fragment of a grave relief (10): the dead woman may have been represented seated (she is lost), while her afflicted husband, a bearded man, stands before her with clasped hands, leaning on his staff. (It is covered by his cloak.) He is Lamprokles, from the deme (district) of Hagnous in Attica. Note traces of painted leaf ornament on the edge and on the capital.

On the expressive *grave relief (4)* the dead woman is seen, like Mnesarete (Room IV: 1), seated in her chamber and grasping the edge of her mantle with one hand; in the other she may be holding a little bird (the relief is weathered). The maid standing before her is carrying a small chest with a gable-shaped lid such as perhaps held jewellery or some household articles.   *Pl. 20* *Pl. 19*

The *West Greek relief (5)* was probably for a music teacher. He is playing a lyre and has his eyes on a boy who sings, reading the music from a scroll.

The *high relief (7)* and *fragmentary relief (11)* each came from a so-called "naïskos" or miniature "temple", a large open-fronted structure composed of separate slabs – narrow ones for the side walls and a broad one for the back, with a fourth slab resting upon them to form the roof. – The relief with a veiled woman laying her right hand on her cheek in a gesture of grief (7) formed the left side slab of an East Greek naïskos. The dead man or woman would have been portrayed, perhaps in company, on the back slab of the naïskos, which joined the preserved relief at right angles at its right-hand end. – The fragment with the head of a lamenting maiden *(11)* comes from the back slab of an Attic naïskos.

The very large *lekythos of Eukoline (9)* shows the dead woman in her family circle: left, her father or father-in-law Chaireas leaning on the back of her chair; then her husband with sword and helmet extending his hand to his wife, as does their little boy; right, a servant with the baby.

The *banquet relief (12)* from East Greece shows a man reclining on a couch ("kliné") at the foot of which sits his wife. The little table in front of them with fruit and other dishes has three ornamental legs in the form of deer feet.

ROOMS VII–IX: SCULPTURES FROM THE SANCTUARY OF APHAIA ON THE ISLAND OF AEGINA

VII Room of the West Pediment Group

1 The West pediment group, 505/500 B. C. (Reconstruction fig. 21; Plates 22–24, 28–29)
2 Warrior's head from West pediment group (Warrior III, Plate 23)
3 Shield and arm of a warrior from West pediment group (Warrior X; shield device fig. 22)
4 Arms of an archer from the sanctuary, 505/500 B. C.
5 Central akroterion from the West façade of temple (partly restored; reconstruction fig. 18), 505/500 B. C.
6 Capital from a column of the temple (from the internal colonnade; reconstruction fig. 15)

VIII Room of the Sphinx

1 Sphinx (torso), akroterion of northwest corner of temple roof, 505/500 B. C.
2 Marble antefix from edge of roof on long side of temple (see reconstruction of temple fig. 15), ca. 500 B. C.
3 Central akroterion from the sanctuary (restored), 505/500 B. C.
4 Inventory from the sanctuary (marble pillar), ca. 410 B. C.

IX Room of the East Pediment Group

1 The East pediment group, 485/480 B. C. (Reconstruction figs. 20, 16; Plates 25–27)
2 Head of warrior from East pediment group (Archer X)
3 Head of Warrior from East pediment group (Warrior IX, comrade of VIII; Plate 25)
4 Head of sphinx, akroterion of northeast corner of temple roof (cover photo), 485/480 B. C. (Reconstruction of temple front fig. 16)

Case A

Fragments from West pediment group of Aegina temple (505/500 B. C.; reconstruction fig. 21): 1. arm of Warrior XII; 3. up-

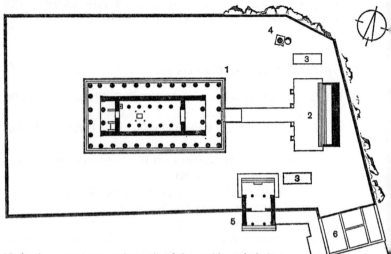

14. Aegina, sanctuary and temple of the goddess Aphaia

per arm of Warrior III; 4. fist of Warrior IX; 5. arm of Warrior II; 6. arm of Warrior X; 13. leg of Warrior VI .

Other pieces: 2. fragment of shield with relief (from East pediment?); 7. two quivers (one perhaps from Archer X on East pediment).

Fragments of sculpture from sanctuary of Aphaia (505/500 B. C.): 8. foot of kneeling figure; 9. foot of an archer (?); 12. foot and drapery of an Athene; 11. Fragment of statuette of a maiden from central akroterion of the East façade of temple (485/480 B. C.; reconstruction of temple front fig. 16).

10. Arm from statue of Athene from the temple (505/500 B. C.; cast from original in National Museum, Athens).

Case B

Fragments from East pediment group of Aegina temple (485/480 B. C.; reconstruction fig. 20): 1. fragment of upper part of body of Archer X; 2. arm of Warrior VIII; 3. fist of Warrior VII; 4. hand of Athene I; 5. forearm of Warrior III; 6. upper arm of Warrior VII.

Fragments from a group from the sanctuary (505/500 B. C.;
reconstruction fig. 23); 7–9 maiden's drapery with feet, forearm
and fragment of sleeve; 10. arm and hand of a second maiden.

Architectural elements from Aegina temple: 11. fragment of
an architrave block (reconstruction of temple figs. 15, 16);
12. cover-tile from roof ridge of temple (reconstruction fig. 19).

The large Rooms VII and IX on the north side of the Glyptothek
(former reception rooms, see p. 12) and the small vestibule VIII
between them are devoted to the pediment groups from the temple
of the goddess Aphaia and to other sculptures etc. belonging to
her temple and precinct.

The sanctuary of Aphaia

The cult of Aphaia on a mountain ridge on the island of Aegina
goes back to the 14th century B. C., and she had already been
worshipped there for more than 700 years when in about 580
B. C. the first great stone temple was built. But when the roof of
that temple burnt it had to be replaced by a second temple. Building began ca. 510 and was completed ca. 480 with an interval of a
decade between 500 and 490. The west pediment belongs to the
first building period of the temple, the east pediment to the second. Simultaneously with the building, the whole sanctuary
(i. e. sacred precinct) was also laid out afresh (reconstructed plan
fig. 14): a columned gateway (5) led from the south on to an
enclosed level terrace with retaining walls. In the middle stood
the temple (1; length 30.5 metres, width 15.5, height 12.4). To the
east stood a large altar for burnt offerings with a paved space in
front of it, four bases, probably for statues, and a paved ramp
leading up to the temple (2). North and south of the altar are
foundations (3) of what must have been two open buildings for
groups of sculpture, and to the north again, near the mouth of a
cistern, stood the only monument from the old sanctuary, a
mighty column crowned by a sphinx (4; height ca. 14 m; ca. 600
B. C.). To the southeast adjoining the precinct there was an administration building with several rooms (6).

This fine sanctuary proves the high regard in which the Aeginetans held their goddess. Aphaia was worshipped only on Aegina
and this was her only shrine. Yet with the conquest of the island
by Athens, the loss of its freedom and prosperity and the expul-

15. Aegina temple (after E. Fiechter)

sion of the old aristocracy (431 B. C.) the shrine was soon to lose its importance. The rites finally fell out of use in the 3rd century B. C. and the neglected temple, whose ruins today greet the approaching voyager from afar, must gradually have fallen prey to dilapidation and overgrowth.

Inventory of the shrine (Room VIII: 4)

A marble pillar found in the temple with an inventory drawn up by Athenian officials attests, though incompletely, to the impoverishment of the sanctuary towards the end of the 5th century B. C. The text preserved reads:" ... chains, 2; iron from an aperture, 2; tongs, 2. Of wood the following: ointment box, 1; chests, 3; scaffolding around the statue complete; throne, 1; stool, 1; stands, 4; small throne, 1; small couch, 1; stand with a back, 1; small boxes, 3; stand for mixing-bowl, 1; small wide chest, 1. In administration building the following: bronze cauldron, 1; handbasin, 1; bowls, 2; axe, 1; doorbolt, 1; knives, 3; couches, 2; bronze washing-up bowl, 1; measure, 1; strainer, 1."

The temple (ground-plan fig. 14; perspective drawing fig. 15 after E. Fiechter 1906).

The temple, of Doric type, was an edifice of the highest order, intended as a magnificent and resplendent house for the deity. As such it in no way resembled the houses of mortals. It was more a built shrine than a house, and like a statue it stood on a base (with three steps). Its interior, a long windowless "cella" lying east-west, did not represent a real room nor did it serve as a place of assembly for the worshippers; rather it was a kind of walled box whose exterior was dignified by a diadem of 30 columns. There were also pairs of columns between the projecting walls at each end of the cella, and the cella walls were adorned on the inside by two rows of five columns, each supporting a row of five smaller ones above an architrave. The *capital (6)* exhibited in Room VII came from one of these smaller rows.

A coating of very fine white plaster covered the limestone structure, the columns with their capitals, the architrave above them (see fragment of an architrave block with strips of regula and guttae, Room IX, Case B: 11) and the projecting cornice of the roof (cf. section and elevation of the east façade fig. 16. The plaster coating of the capital Room VII: 6 is now slightly yellowed). The upper part of the temple was more colourful: horizontal elements, such as the neck-rings of the columns and the crowning ribbon ("taenia") of the architrave, were painted red, while black was used for vertical elements like the triply-moulded "triglyphs". The spaces between the triglyphs, called "metopes", may once have been filled by wooden plaques painted or covered with bronze reliefs. And the triangular pediments terminating the ridged roof – where the groups of sculpted figures stood as if on a narrow stage shut off by stone slabs from the roofwork within – were brilliant with colour. The upper surface of the horizontal cornice or "geison" of the pediments, on which the figures rested, was painted red to represent the earth, the background of the pediments cobalt blue for sky. Even the figures themselves were painted in a variety of colours (cf. p. 62).

So too were the sculptures on the roof – the central "akroteria" on the roof-ridge at each end (i. e. above each pediment) in the form of plants flanked by maidens, and the four sphinxes at the corners.

The sculptures of the pediments and on the roof were conceived as part and parcel of the architectonic whole and gave it its freest

16. Aegina, east façade of the temple

expression. These temple sculptures were wrought from the fine-grained marble quarried on the island of Paros.

The cult statues in the cella of temple

Unauthorised persons were kept out of the temple interior by high grilles between the columns and by the bolted portals of the cella (cf. figs. 14, 15). Inside the cella stood two cult statues – the ancient statue of Aphaia presumably a wooden image ("xoanon") whose stone base in the northwest corner still survives, and in the middle of the cella, a statue of Athene, armed and more than lifesize, which was made for this temple, 505/500 B. C. Traces of its base can still be seen on the floor along with postholes for the wooden railing surrounding it, which is mentioned in the inventory (cf. ground-plan fig. 14; inventory Room VIII: 4; pp. 48 f.).

The *right arm of the statue of Athene* is preserved (Room IX; Case A: 10, cast from the original in the National Museum, Athens. Upper arm has a hole for the dowel for attachment to the figure). The statue was partly bronze, partly marble ("acrolithic"). The drapery, aegis, helmet, shield and lance were of bronze, the head and the arms and feet (affixed separately) of marble. The warlike goddess grasped the shaft of a lance in her upraised right

17. Bronze statuette of
Athene (480 B. C.)

arm (cf. fig. 17 after a bronze statuette of Athene in the National
Museum, Athens). – In the cella of the temple there was also
discovered a large ivory eye with inlaid iris (now lost), probably
of coloured glass, and a bronze "button" for the pupil (Room I X
Case A; 7th century B. C.).

The central akroteria: "volute trees" with small statues of maidens
The central akroterion (Room VII: 5) stood above the West pediment of the temple. It has been put together to about half its
height from fragments and partly restored (additional fragments
in Aegina Museum; see reconstruction fig. 18). Two stems spring
from a heavy apex-block which rested on the roof-ridge. They
curl upwards back and forth, sprouting volutes and little palmettes
until they blossom into the final palmette at the top. Together
with the apex-block the akroterion stood about 2 metres high.
It was chiselled from a single large block of marble and was
steadied against the force of the wind by a support in the form of a
roughly modelled lion (cf. fig. 16. Apex-block is a cast, with missing parts restored, from the original in Aegina Museum). The
volute tree is flanked by two attractive maidens gathering up
their drapery.

18. Aegina, central akroterion
from west façade of temple
(Room VII: 5). Maidens flank-
ing volute tree are shown in
outline.

There was a similar central akroterion over the East pediment
(fragment of one maiden, Room IX, Case A: 11; some fragments
from the volute tree are in Aegina Museum).

A third *volute tree (Room VIII: 3)*, now restored complete,
was originally designed as the East central akroterion, but
after the interruption of the building of the temple it was
rejected and was set up in the precinct in front of the temple
as a votive offering to the goddess. The individual leaves
of this sumptuous palmette were worked in relief on the front
surface, while on the back they were painted (traces still visible).

The corner akroteria: sphinxes

Torso of a sphinx (Room VIII: 1). At once demonic and lovable,
gentle and severe, these heavenly creatures with hound's body
and limbs and maiden's head stood guard over the temple, crouching at the four corners of the roof. This one comes from the
northwest corner. From the northeast corner we have a beautiful
maiden's head from a sphinx (Room IX: 4; picture on cover), exceptionally well preserved. She wears a graceful diadem in her thick,
closely waved hair and little disc earrings.

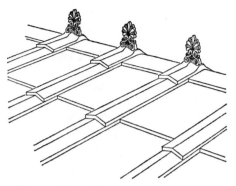

19. Aegina, detail of temple roof showing pan- and cover-tiles and palmette antefixes on roofridge (Room IX, Case B: 12)

The temple roof

The roof of the temple was covered by tiles of two kinds – large, flat rectangular pan-tiles and bent cover-tiles, triangular in section, which covered the sidejoints between the pan-tiles. All of these were of terracotta except for the outermost row along the edges of the roof: these were of marble (cf. fig. 15). In Room VIII are exhibited some *marble cover-tiles (2)* terminating in palmette antefixes with traces of painting on the leaves. Painted palmettes from the terracotta cover-tiles which adorned the roof-ridge in a continuous row are to be found in Room IX, Case B: 12 (cf. fig.19).

The pediment groups from the Aegina temple

The sculpted groups of the two pediments set up on 11.70 metre long bases in Rooms VII and IX are the museum's most precious possessions and so are fittingly housed at the building's centre. The West pediment group, which originally had 13 figures, is the better preserved (VII: 1; reconstruction fig. 21). Of the 11 original figures of the East pediment group the most coherent sequence of figures comes from the right hand side (IX: 1; reconstruction fig. 20; cf. fig. 16, which shows its relation to the temple as a whole). Various larger pieces which could not be set up within the groups are displayed on separate pedestals: in Room VII a warrior's head and a shield from the West pediment group (VII: Pl. 23   2, 3); in Room IX two warriors' heads from the East pediment Pl. 25   group (IX: 2, 3). Some additional fragments from both groups

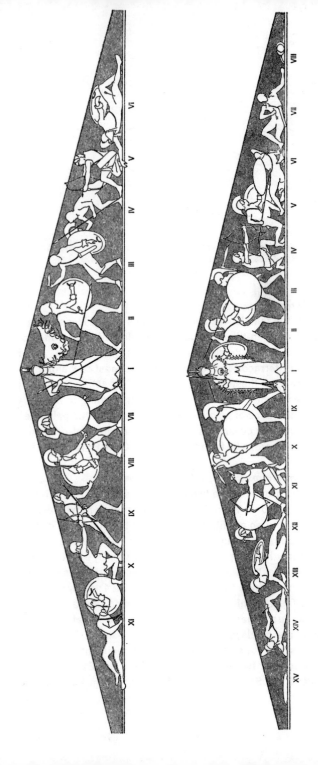

20–21. Aegina, east and west pediment groups (Rooms IX and VIII)

are to be seen in Cases A and B in Room IX. Certain parts of both pediments are casts, the originals being in the Aegina Museum or the National Museum, Athens.

The Aegina figures are the best preserved of all such Greek temple groups, with the sole exception of those from the mighty temple of Zeus at Olympia made a few decades later and now in the Olympia Museum. As the most comprehensive monument of Greek sculpture from the turn of the 6th and 5th centuries, they are priceless evidence for the vitally important process of transition which was taking place in Greek art at that time (cf. pp. 24 f.). Without them, moreover, we should know next to nothing of the Aeginetan school of sculpture so much admired by the ancients.

To be commissioned with adorning the house of a deity with large-scale works of art was a very rare and honourable privilege for a sculptor. It must have been the most respected Aeginetan artists of their day who after careful selection were chosen to design the sculptures for the pediments and roof. The actual work of sculpting the marble they did partly with their own hands and partly with the help of assistants from their workshops. The master who did the West pediment group at the end of the 6th century remains unknown to us by name. But the second man, who after the long interruption was commissioned in the 480's with the sculptures of the East (main) façade was perhaps the leading Aeginetan sculptor of the new epoch, Onatas. The East pediment group may be the most important work from the early part of his career (cf. statue of Apollo Room III: 3, p. 25).

Discovery, first restoration and present arrangement
(documents in Room VIII)

It was in the year 1811 that the temple sculptures and fragments of other sculptures from the sanctuary were discovered in the lonely ruins (first mentioned by an English traveller in 1675) by a party of four young scholars and artists who had come to Aegina in order to draw and measure the temple. They were the Bavarian architect Carl Haller von Hallerstein, the English architects Charles Robert Cockerell and John Foster and the Swabian Jacob Linckh. Their find was a happy coincidence, for the ruins were beginning to be used (not for the first time) as a quarry and the sculptures stood in danger of being largely destroyed. Shipped via Athens and the islands of Zakynthos and Malta they arrived in Rome. Meanwhile King Ludwig I of Bavaria had purchased the whole find through his art agent Johann Martin von Wagner, and now at Rome on King Ludwig's orders Wagner was made responsible for getting the torsos – and only the torsos – restored. All the missing heads and limbs, as well as other missing or damaged parts, were replaced or patched in marble according to models made by the Danish sculptor Berthel Thorvaldsen. (The restored figures were also provided with bronze weapons.) The maidens from the west central akroterion (VII:5) and the sphinx torso (VIII:1) were restored in the same way, the sphinx being turned into a griffin in the process.

Thus completed down to the last detail and supported on iron rods, 10 figures (of the original 13) from the West pediment group and only 5 (of 11) from the East were installed in the newly-built Glyptothek. The present-day Room III (Room of Diomede) was named the "Ägineten-Saal" in their honour, and here they were set up on two bases of equal length facing each other across the room, the figures of each group being disposed in a purely decorative scheme. For no-one in Rome had considered the most urgent question, how did the figures fit together? Their Greek creators had not conceived them as a more or less random row of separate forms but as a single organism composed of a complex of numerous inter-related parts which together made up a triangular pediment-shaped whole. Many individual fragments give clues to the composition, but they were disregarded.

The restoration aroused criticism almost as soon as it was finished, though it also had many admirers, for the new heads and limbs, modelled on existing originals even down to the weathering of the marble surface, were indeed a remarkable feat of imitation. But it was condemned with increasing freguency as a serious stylistic misconception and as misleading with respect to the figures' original unity. Adolf Furtwängler (who was Director of the museum 1894–1907 and excavated the sanctuary in 1901) called the restoration "the darkest hour in the Aegina figures' history". Ernst Buschor after the War called in emphatic terms for the "rescue of the Aeginetans", Hans Diepolder pressed for its accomplishment and all right-minded friends and connoisseurs of Greek art spoke up for the removal of the modern additions and a new arrangement of the pedimental groups.

As a result of these repeated demands, the new exhibition was worked out in the years 1962–5. This involved making use of all the available interlocking clues afforded by Furtwängler's and Eduard Schmidt's researches, supplemented by the researches of recent years. There was, for example, evidence from the architecture of the pediments and their measurements (length and height of the triangular spaces 13.20 and 1.74 metres), from the beddings for the figures' plinths on the partly preserved blocks of the horizontal geison of the pediments (cf. p. 49) and from the variations in the weathering of the marble, which is of course more pronounced on the exposed "outside" surfaces, the ones facing the spectator. All previously disregarded fragments, the number of which had been increased by the excavations on the site, had to be taken into consideration and hitherto unnoticed joins indicated. Above all, the gestures and actions of the figures, better or worse preserved as they might be, had to be sorted out so as to establish a lifelike sequence and put the "actors" into their original and logical relationships with one another, disentangled from the incomplete or quite misunderstood motivation which the 19th century restoration had given them.

The mythical scenes

The world of the gods and the legends of the mythical forefathers whose origin and destiny were so bound up with the gods offered the only possible subjects for the decoration of a Greek temple. On the pediments of the temple of Aphaia the theme is the battles fought by Aeginetan ancestral heroes during the first and second campaigns against the Anatolian city of Troy.

The East pediment – being the most important side, facing the altar – told the more important story, that of the first campaign, which was untertaken by Telamon and his friend Herakles, the greatest hero of Greece. Telamon was the father of Ajax and son of Aeacus, first king of Aegina and ancestor of the family of the Aeacids. Like Herakles, Aeacus was a son of Zeus; his mother was the river nymph Aegina, who gave the island its name (cf. p. 65 for sculptures from the precinct representing the abduction of Aegina by Zeus). When Telamon and Herakles stormed Troy, Herakles with his arrows slew the Trojan king Laomedon and all his sons but one, the future king Priam.

The theme of the West pediment is a battle during the second siege of Troy, the siege in which Aeacus's descendants took part. Prominent among them was Ajax, Telamon's son, Herakles's "godson" and grandson of Zeus. He was particularly honoured in Aegina. The poet Pindar, who at the time the temple was being built must frequently have visited Aegina as a friend of the Aeginetan nobility and who wrote a processional song for the goddess Aphaia (perhaps indeed for the dedication of her new temple), celebrated in his victory songs for young local athletes their ancestors' twofold struggle for Troy.

It is best to look at the East pediment first (Room IX):

The East pediment group (Room IX: 1 and 2–3; fragments Case B: 1–6. Reconstruction fig. 20)

In the centre of the pediment – directing the operations, so to speak – stands the goddess Athene (I: head, feet, fragment from upper part of body). She is striding to the right, but her gaze is directed "out" towards the beholder. – On each side of her a front-rank champion leads the attack. The Aeacid Telamon is the one on the left (VII: part of right leg; right fist, upper part of left arm with part of shield Case B: 3, 6). The man on the right (II) is a Trojan, perhaps Priam, at whom Athene is brandishing her aegis with its writhing snakes (left hand of Athene with part of aegis Case B: 4; the snakes around the edge of the aegis were worked separately in marble and fitted on). – The opponents (III and VIII) of these two champions are getting the worst of the duel and have been wounded. The Greek on the right side (III) has chest wounds, realistically chiselled. He is losing his shield as he stumbles, backwards, for his left arm has gone limp (right forearm Case B: 5). Telamon's Trojan opponent is staggering back in the same manner (VIII: legs; left arm with shield-stay Case B: 2). A companion rushes up to the aid of each of these hard-pressed fighters (III and VIII). The Greek (IV) is bringing the helmet his lord (III) has lost in the fighting: his right hand grasps the cheek-piece. The Trojan on the left (IX: both legs), who has come to help Telamon's opponent (VIII), may have been holding a lance. His exceptionally well preserved head is displayed on a separate pedestal (Room IX: 3).   *Pl. 25*

Then follow archers. The armed man on the right (V) with the lion's-head helmet is Telamon's friend Herakles. The left hand   *Pl. 27*

archer wearing a chiton over his armour is another Trojan (X: left
leg; fragment with drapery from the chest, Case B: 1; one of the
quivers Case A: 7 may be his). His head is exhibited on a separate
base (Room IX: 2). – In the corners lie two dying victims (VI and
XI) of the far-shooting bowmen. The kingly bearded figure at the

Pl. 26 left end is the Trojan king **Laomedon** (XI). One of Herakles's
arrows has got him in the chest and his arm is sliding limply out
of the shield-stay. Only with the help of the sword in his right
hand can he hold himself up any longer. The youthful Greek with
an arrow in his thigh was sinking to the ground with his right arm
outstretched (VI in right corner: head, legs and left hand; chest
etc. reconstructed).

The West pediment group (Room VII: 1 and 2–3; fragments Room
IX Case A: 1, 3–6, 13. Reconstruction fig. 21)

Here again, as on the East pediment, the central place is taken by

Pl. 22 Athene (I) as the goddess who determines the battle's outcome.
But here, instead of striding forth and taking an active part, she is
standing still and facing straight forward. – On either side of her
is a pair of warriors – champions II and IX and their opponents III
and X who are being beaten back. The champion on the left (IX)

Pl. 24 is Zeus's grandson Ajax, the son of the Telamon on the East pediment (right fist Room IX Case A: 4). His shield bore as device
(painted on – note traces of faded paint) an eagle with a snake in
its beak, the sign by which, as Pindar says, Zeus announced
Ajax's birth. The well preserved shield of Ajax's opponent X
(right arm Room IX Case A: 6) is displayed on a separate pedestal. From the traces of faded paint one can clearly make out its
device, the forepart of a springing boar (Room VII: 3; fig. 22). –
The right hand champion II (right arm Room IX Case A: 5) is, as
on the East pediment, a Trojan. His opponent's head, an excellent
piece of work and in good condition, is again displayed on a sepa-

Pl. 23 rate pedestal (Warrior III, Room VII: 2. Legs and upper arm with
part of shield Room IX Case A: 3).
Then follow on each side four warriors forming two interwoven
pairs. IV and XI are archers, and their victims VII and XIV lie
wounded in the corners of the pediment. Between them on each
side is a crouching warrior (V and XII) and his fallen opponent
who tries to cover himself with his shield (VI and XIII). – Both
archers are wearing armour. The left-hand one XI in the foreign,

Scythian-style leather cuirass must be Paris, the son and grand-   *Pl. 29*
son respectively of Priam and Laomedon, the Trojan kings who
appear on the East pediment. In the man on the right (IV) we
should recognise Ajax's brother Teucer, for Teucer and Paris
are the two great bowmen of the Second Trojan War. – Paris's
victim in the left-hand corner (XIV) has an arrow in the thigh like
the dying Greek on the East pediment (VI); the Trojan on the
extreme right (VII), like the Trojan king Laomedon in the East
pediment (XI), has been pierced in the breast by an arrow. – Out
in the farthest corners of the pediment lie two objects: right, the
helmet of the wounded Trojan (VIII, crest preserved); left, the
shield of the wounded Greek (XV; fragments once existed but
are now lost). – From the fallen Warrior VI in the right-hand group
of hand-to-hand fighters we have the left leg (Room IX Case A:
13; fragments of the right hand, which was clutching a stone on
the ground, are in Aegina Museum). A right arm (Room IX
Case A: 1) belonged to the crouching Warrior XII in the left-hand
group.

Interpretation, costume and armour

The message of the pediment groups is not the glorification of
war and of the winning side, for Greeks and Trojans are equally
matched (East pediment: Greeks VII, III–VI; Trojans II, VIII–XI.
West pediment: Greeks IX, XIII–XIV, III–V; Trojans II, VI–VII,
XI–XII). Rather the key to their meaning is the Greek concept of
"agon" or "athlos", which conveys the notions of struggle, burning
endeavour, urgency, reward for valour, as well as danger in battle
or athletic contests.

On each pediment there are a number of warriors who can be
singled out as individuals. Herakles on the East pediment and   *Pl. 27*
Paris and Teucer on the West can be recognised by their dress   *Pl. 29*
and method of fighting, Ajax on the West by his shield device,
Laomedon on the East because he is matched against Herakles,
Telamon as one of the champions by the side of Athene, Priam
as the other, whom she is threatening. It is conceivable that the
names of the figures were also painted on the front of the pedimental geison.

Athene on both pediments appears with helmet and lance, wearing a long "chiton" and a "himation" and sandals originally with
painted thongs. On the West pediment the mantle (himation) she

wears passes crosswise under her left breast. Her aegis covers her shoulders and bosom and hangs down behind her back. From the edge of the aegis emerge countless writhing serpents (carved and attached separately) and the aegis itself is covered with scales (traces of painting visible). The Gorgon's head on the front was likewise executed separately and the holes for its attachment can still be seen. On her left arm the West pediment goddess bears a shield. On the East pediment however Athene has slung her aegis over her left arm instead and is using it as a weapon, shaking it threateningly at Priam on her left (II = Priam. Left hand of Athene with part of aegis Room IX: Case B: 4).

The representation of the warriors is above the plane of everyday reality. Few of them wear body-armour, only the four archers (East pediment V = Herakles and X; West IV = Teucer and XI =

Pl. 29 Paris) and perhaps also Telamon's opponent, who at least was wearing greaves (East pediment VIII). Priam's opponent (East pediment III) on the other hand wears greaves on his shins but is otherwise quite naked, as are most of the figures.

The helmets are of various kinds, with and without cheek-pieces and nose-guard. Some are pulled down over the forehead, as was

Pl. 26 customary in close fighting (e. g. East pediment XI = Laomedon), but the cheek-pieces, which protect the face, have here and there been put up (e. g. East pediment IX). On other figures the helmet has been pushed back, leaving the face free (e. g. East pediment

Pl. 24 II = Priam, West IX = Ajax). The shields, six in number on the East pediment and eight on the West, are important elements in the composition, but few have survived to any great extent and many are missing altogether (but in some places restored).

Pieces worked separately in marble

Every figure was carved from a single large block of marble (e. g., East pediment, Laomedon XI and Priam II with their shields; West pediment, Warrior II with his shield; Ajax = IX and Athene with shields and crested helmets). Heads and limbs were in no case attached separately. But shields, because of the risk of breakage, were often ground thin on a wheel first and then set on (East pediment III, VI, VIII; West V, XII, XIII). A good many other elements were worked separately for reasons not always easy to see: e. g. on the East pediment crest and cheek-pieces of

Pl. 26 Laomedon's helmet (XI), serpents on Athene's aegis (I; hand

with part of aegis Room IX: Case B: 4), Priam's shield-strap (II),
helmet in hand of Warrior IV, lappets on Herakles's cuirass and
lion's fangs on his helmet (V); on the West pediment details on   *Pl. 27*
Paris's leather cap (XI), serpents and Gorgon-head on Athene's   *Pl. 29*
aegis (I), lappets on Teucer's cuirass (IV). The weapons etc. –
swords, sheaths, bows, quivers – were also executed separately
(two quivers Room IX, Case A: 7; fragments of weapons in
Aegina Museum).

Separately worked pieces in metal

Besides the marble attachments there were some in metal.
Arrows and probably the lances were of bronze, while lead was
used presumably for the baldricks of sword-sheaths and quivers
and certainly here and there for curls and locks of hair (e. g. hair
visible beneath the helmets of IX and of the dying Warrior VI
from the East pediment; hair at nape of IX = Ajax from the West
pediment; long hanging locks of both Athenes and her forehead
hair, East pediment; pubic hair, probably of Priam = II, East pediment). More precious metals probably served for the two Athenes'
earrings and for helmet decorations such as those of the West
pediment Athene and Warrior III.

Painting

The colouring, now visible only in occasional traces on the
weathered surface, contributed in no small part to the effect of
the pediments. The red earth and blue sky have already been
mentioned (see p. 49). But the figures themselves, including the
lead details, must have been painted. Lips, eyes and hair, pubic
hair, garments and their borders, Athene's scaled aegis (see
traces on back of West pediment aegis), body-armour (traces
on Paris's leather cuirass, West pediment XI), helmets (net
pattern East pediment IX, Room VII: 3), weapons and shields   *Pl. 25*
(shield devices West pediment: eagle, Ajax IX; boar, Ajax's
opponent X, Room VII: 3, fig. 22). There was similar painting on
the akroteria, as on the volute trees with maidens and the sphinxes
(cf. pp. 51 f. and front cover).

State of preservation

Although visible only from the front, the figures were worked
with equal care and attention to detail all the way round, even

22. Aegina, west pediment group:
    shield of Warrior X with painted
    device of a boar (Room VII: 3)

down to the painting (e. g., on West pediment, scales on Athene's aegis, shield devices of Warriors II and X).

The back of the figures, where the marble surface was protected from weathering, is as a rule excellent. So too is the front of the lower parts (feet, lower legs), thanks to the early impoverishment and neglect of the temple, for the earth and vegetation accumulated so soon around them safeguarded them from wind and rain.

The East and West pediments compared

In the sculptures of the East and West pediments we see the same mythological material presumably handled by two masters of two generations directly consecutive in time but separated stylistically by the profoundest gap. The "West pediment master", who worked in the closing years of the 6th century, precedes the revolution which set in at the turn of the century (cf. pp. 24f.). He was one of the last sculptors to belong to the archaic tradition and his pediment (fig. 21) still radiates the freshness and *Pls.5,7* joie de vivre we saw in the kouroi in Room I (Room I: 1, 2). Though his figures present a great variety of movements and postures of the human form – attacking, defending themselves, kneeling, falling – nonetheless their movement manifests the same restraint and unshakeable self-containment as the stiff, erect youths in Room I. The mighty "agon" being played out before Troy is recorded with an untroubled, one might almost say cheerful, self-confidence, and the colourful, many-figured composition delights us in the same way as an intricate, half-solemn, half-lyric verse picture. The attitudes and gestures please the eye with their arresting outlines, whose position and interlacing creates the effect of a patterned net. The "West pediment master" saw the triangular pediment space as a hollowed-out field which he must fill up with a pattern of figures. He used the space artistically but his figure-group bears no real relation to it.

On the East pediment the space is opened up (fig. 20). It no longer serves simply as the background to a flat pattern of figures but rather as the atmosphere, the stage, in which the figures are acting out a unified dramatic event. The triangular space is filled with a rhythmic composition and its width and depth brought into play, while the figures themselves are fewer in number than on the West pediment and have become larger and more massive. The "East pediment master", working in the second decade of the 5th century (after the interval during which work on the temple was suspended, cf. p. 55), was a pioneer of the new "classical" epoch. In his figures there is none of the colourful, naive cheerfulness of the earlier master. They act of their own free will, doing and suffering in the shadow of self-awareness.

The contrast between the two pediments may be seen in individual warriors but principally in the groups engaged in direct combat. Compare, for example, the first dramatically connected figures on the right half of the East pediment (II–IV: Priam, his staggering opponent, the latter's companion hurrying to his aid from the "depths" of the pediment) with the group of four Warriors on the outer left side of the West (XI–XIV: Paris, one warrior ducking and two fallen). Or compare two bowmen, Herakles (East *Pl. 27* pediment V) and Paris (West pediment XI). Herakles draws his *Pl. 29* bow with a solid massive effort that makes Paris seem almost light-hearted and weightless. Again, the Trojan king Laomedon, *Pl. 26* wounded by Herakles's arrow, is portrayed on the East pediment as a man sinking beneath the burden of his inescapable fate. The "West pediment master" makes him simply a wounded man (VII, right end) without weightier cares.

Warrior group and group with Zeus and Aegina from the precinct of the Aegina sanctuary (Room VII: 4 and Room IX Cases A and B)

In addition to the pediment groups there were found fragments from two other groups, which were set up in the precinct in front of the East façade of the temple; one group with fighting warriors

23. Aegina, group with Zeus and the nymph Aegina (fragments in
Room IX, Case B)

(warriors and Amazons?) in the presence of Athene; the other
depicts the abduction by Zeus of the nymph Aegina. From their
style it is clear that both were made in the late 6th century, and
from their workmanship it seems that both were carved out in the
workshop of the "West pediment master" (505/500 B. C.). The
dimensions correspond to those of the West pediment figures.
Warrior group. Two arms are preserved from an archer drawing
his bow (Room VII: 4). The figure wore Scythian-style leather

Pl. 29 armour like the West pediment Paris (XI) and was no doubt meant
for a foreign warrior (or Amazon). A right foot and one of the two
quivers (Room IX Case A: 7, 9) probably also belonged to it. The
fragment of the Athene is exhibited in the same place (12). (In the
National Museum, Athens, and the Aegina Museum there are
further fragments – four heads of warriors, hands etc.)
The group with Zeus and Aegina tells the story of Zeus's abduction
of the nymph Aegina, one of the numerous daughters of the
Peloponnesian river-god Asopus. The nymph, after whom the
island had its name, bore Zeus a son, Aeacus, who became the
first king of Aegina. It was his son and grandsons who waged the
two campaigns against Troy which are portrayed on the pediments of the temple (cf. pp. 57f.). The surviving fragments are
shown in Room IX Case B: feet of Aegina with part of drapery (7),
her left forearm and sleeve (8), fragment of her right sleeve (9),
left arm of one of her sisters (10). These are shown hatched in the
reconstruction, fig. 23, based on an Attic vase-painting of Zeus,
Aegina and three of her sisters (Metropolitan Museum of Art,
New York). The three central figures form a closely interwoven

group with Zeus brandishing his thunderbolt, Aegina touching his beard in supplication and the sister to whom she reaches out with her other hand for protection. To tie them together the sculptor worked Aegina's forearms separately and attached them later (Room IX Case B: 8–9: left forearm with surfaces for attachment on both sides; right sleeve with hole for a dowel for affixing the forearm). One can get some idea of the excellence of the work from the delicate hand of the sister plucking at her mantle as she flees towards the right (Room IX Case B: 10).

It is clear from these fragments that when the temple was begun two themes from Aeginetan legend were chosen for the pediments and that not only were designs submitted but a number of figures were actually completed. The subjects were the myth of the divine origin of the Aeacids and a battle, perhaps Telamon's and Herakles's campaign against the Amazons.

But both these groups by the "West pediment master", which were not used for the final version of the temple pediment remained the goddess's property. They were set up in two open-fronted structures specially built for their display (for foundations of these structures see p. 47 and ground-plan of sanctuary fig. 14 no. 3). A central akroterion likewise intended for the East pediment and probably from his workshop was also displayed in the precinct (volute tree Room VIII: 3, pp. 51 f.).

1   Alexander ("Alexander Rondanini"), copy of a work by Euphranor (338/336 B. C. Plate 31)

2   Demosthenes (herm), copy after a statue by Polyeuktos (280 B. C.)

3   Poet or philosopher. Copy of a statue (380/360 B. C.)

4   Head of Herakles? Ca. 320 B. C.

5   Grave relief of Hiras son of Nikanor. From Erythrae in western Asia Minor, ca. 100 B. C.

6   Grave relief of Nikolaos of Miletus, son of Euodos, 1st century A. D.

7   Gravestone of Eutaktos. From Paros? 2nd century A. D.

8   Honorary document from Apollonia-on-the-Rhyndacus, northern Asia Minor, 40 A. D.

9   Large head of a goddess (Aphrodite?), copy from a statue (250/200 B. C. Plate 30)

10   Female torso. Copy of an East Greek statue (ca. 130 B. C.)

11   Torso of a woman moving forward, 410/390 B. C.

12   Roman relief with scene of sacrifice, 1st century A. D.

Pl. 31

In the middle of Room X (northeast corner of the Glyptothek) stands the *"Alexander Rondanini" (1)*, so named from the Palazzo Rondanini in Rome, where it was once housed. This is one of the most impressive contemporary portraits of the great Macedonian. (The right leg is a modern restoration.) Numerous portraits made during his lifetime are mentioned by ancient authors – paintings by Apelles (one of which, in the temple of Artemis at Ephesus, showed him as world ruler with thunderbolt and aegis, the attributes of Zeus, king of the gods) and statues by Lysippus, Praxiteles, Leochares and Euphranor. Leochares of Athens and Euphranor of Corinth portrayed him as prince after the battle of Chaeronea. It was this battle, fought in 338 B. C. in Boeotia (central Greece), that made Alexander's father, King Philip II of Macedon, master of Greece, and the young prince had fought at his father's side. Leochares's gold and ivory statues of the royal family were set up like statues of gods in the Philippeion, a round temple still standing in ruins in the sanctuary of Zeus at Olympia. Euphranor's work on the other hand was in

24. Statue of the Athenian orator
Demosthenes (Room X: 2)

bronze and commemorated the battle by showing father and son
in a war chariot drawn by a double team of horses. It was from
this work undoubtedly that our Roman copy, the Alexander
Rondanini, was taken. The young prince is seen as his father's
chariot-driver, gazing into the distance as he grasps the reins
in his outstretched hands, about to mount the chariot after his
father. The portrait is meant to be viewed from the left, where the
movement of the body and of Alexander's head with its characteristic "leonine shock" of hair is developed with the greatest
freedom. (The support in shape of cuirass with mantle was
added by the copyist.)

Portrait of Demosthenes (2). "Had thy strength but equalled thy
purposes, Demosthenes, never had the Greeks been ruled by
Macedon's war-god." Thus ran the inscription on the plinth of
Polyeuktos's portrait of Demosthenes. So much did the ancients
admire this statue that the head is known to us from no fewer
than forty copies. The Glyptothek's example on a herm is one of
these. Of the whole body only two copies are so far known. The
original was a commemorative statue in bronze set up in Demos-

thenes's honour in the market-place of Athens at the request of
his nephew in 280 B. C., 42 years after the great orator's death.
Famous as a speaker in the law-courts and in public affairs,
Demosthenes had worked with untiring energy for the freedom
and independence of Athens and other Greek cities while the
threat of Macedonian rule drew ever nearer. After the death of
Alexander he was implicated in an anti-Macedonian conspiracy
and on being condemned to death took poison. "In his face," said
a later biographer (Plutarch), "there was always a certain intense
earnestness and this thoughtful, anxious look he did not easily
lay aside." With this look he was immortalised for the citizens of
Athens in Polyeuktos's incomparable portrait: his care-lined face
inclined to the right, hands clasped in stern self-control, his tense
figure wasted by ceaseless anxiety and exertion – a real memorial,
combining simplicity with greatness. Even the stiff, simple garment crossing the body in tight folds is part of the likeness. The
individual character and destiny of the man are set forth with a
vividness and attention to detail (seen from close up, as it were)
foreign until then to Greek art, yet the statue transcends these
to become at the same time a picture of the universal human
tragedy. But the Greek principle of portraying the whole man in
a complete statue was not understood by the Roman copyist who
took the head only and grafted it on to the meaningless form of
a herm (Case: small Roman copy of the portrait statue).

The *torso from the statue of a woman (10)* in a mantle so fine-spun
that the folds of the chiton show through beneath it was mentioned
by Adalbert Stifter as the "Maiden from Cumae". What he saw
in Munich in the autumn of 1846 was Thorvaldsen's restored
version, done in 1812 after the removal of 18th-century restorations
by Pacetti. The original on which our copy (perhaps a Roman
portrait statue) was based probably belonged to a group of Muses
from somewhere in East Greece.

The little *female torso (11)* in festive dress and posture almost
certainly comes from a group, conceivably from a group which
stood as central akroterion on the roof of a temple. The position of
the arms suggests she was playing the lyre. Like the statuette of
Athene, Room III: 12, she came to Munich from the Palazzo
Giustiniani-Recanati in Venice (cf. p. 28).

The East Greek *grave relief of Hiras (5)* is inscribed with the names
of the dead man and his father followed by the greeting "chaire"–

"farewell!" Hiras (a poet?) stands before a half-open door in a statuesque and pretentious attitude far removed from the breathing stillness and serenity of the 5th- and 4th-century grave monuments in Rooms IV and VI. The tall hexagonal pedestal against which the heroised dead man lounges supports a cult-pillar with the image perhaps of Dionysus. Two servants are depicted to smaller scale, one holding rolled-up scrolls, the other with his hand laid sadly to his cheek. The decoration on the base consists of sphinxes and of a garland with the skull of a sacrificial bull. Columns support an architrave with frieze of urns, rosettes and winged genii and crowned by a pediment.

On the *gravestone of Eutaktos (7* – child with jug greeting the dead man) the inscription tells us that (Council and) People decreed a golden wreath to Eutaktos son of Eutaktos for his love of his country.

The *honorary inscription (8)* crowned by a pediment with plant ornament tells us of one Saupheios Maker, a priest of the Roman Emperor-cult, who 40 A. D. on his own undertaking organised gymnastic practice for young and old and with the money thus raised established a city food market.

The *Roman relief (12)* shows a priestess (?) standing before a cult vessel ("cista") on a tripod stand; in front of this an incense stand where a man, assisted by a small boy with a jug, makes an offering by sprinkling incense on to the embers from a box.

XI ROOM OF ROMAN PORTRAITS

A. Portraits and a large relief monument from Rome in first bay of Room (cf. p. 76, fig. 25)

1 Bust of Augustus (ruled 31 B. C. – 14 A. D.). Posthumous portrait, 40/50 A. D. (Plate 37)
2 Statue of the Empress Livia, wife of Augustus (torso; draped statue dependent on Greek prototypes of 4th century B. C.) After 14 A. D.
3 Bust of Tiberius (Emperor 14–37 A. D.)
4 Empress Agrippina, wife of Claudius (Emperor 41–54 A. D.), head from a statue
5 Caius Octavius, father of Augustus (?), head from a statue ca. 60 B. C.
6 Bust of a young man, 40/30 B. C. (Plate 34)
7 Head of an old man, ca. 40 B. C.
8 Head of a man, 30/20 B. C.
9 Bust of young woman, 50/60 A. D.
10 Woman with high curled coiffure. Bust, ca. 80 A. D.
11 Bald-headed priest (fragment), ca. 80 A. D.
12 Bust of a man, ca. 90 A. D.
13 "Marius", bust, 50/40 B. C. (Plate 35)
14 "Sulla", 50/40 B. C. Large draped bust modern, added by Alessandro Algardi in the 17th century, when original narrow bust was removed and the head polished.
15 Statue of Roman "imperator" in armour, ca. 70 B. C.
16 Relief frieze from large rectangular monument from Rome. Short sides and first long side: wedding procession of Poseidon and Amphitrite. Second long side (cast from original in Louvre, Paris): Roman public sacrifice in the Campus Martius in Rome. Ca. 70 B. C. (Plate 33)

B. Portraits, gladiator relief and large mosaic in second bay (cf. p. 79, fig. 26)

17 Bust of Trajan (Emperor 98–117 A. D.), 100/110 A. D.
18 Head of a poet, 100/110 A. D.
19 Bust of a man, 110/120 A. D. (Plate 38)
20 Head of a boy. From a statue, 100/110 A. D.

21 Bust of a man, ca. 110 A. D.

22 Head of a man (fragment), ca. 120 A. D.

23 Head of priest wearing cap, ca. 120 A. D.

24 Head of a woman, ca. 100 A. D.

25 Statue of a woman (draped statue after Greek prototype of 3rd century B. C.), 110/130 A. D.

26 Head of woman with tall diadem (perhaps Empress Plotina, wife of Trajan), 100/110 A. D.

27 Head of a woman, 90/100 A. D.

28 Head of Empress Faustina, wife of Marcus Aurelius (reigned 161–180). From Syria, 160/170 A. D.

29 T. Caesernius Statianus, statesman in reigns of Hadrian (117–138) and Antoninus Pius (138–161). Head from a statue in armour (imperator), ca. 130 A. D. (Plate 36)

30 Bust of Antinous, favourite of the Emporer Hadrian, deified after death. 130/135 A. D.

31 Bust of Apollodorus. Probably a posthumous portrait of the master architect of the Emperors Trajan and Hadrian. Ca. 140 A. D.

32 Large bust of Antoninus Pius (Emperor 138–161) in cuirass and cloak (paludamentum). Probably name was once painted on small panel on stand. Ca. 150 A. D.

33 Bust of a man, 130/140 A. D. (Plate 39)

34 Head of a priestess with garland of corn-ears, ca. 140 A. D.

35 Head of a man, ca. 170 A. D.

36 Head of a youthful man, ca. 190 A. D.

37 Head of a man. From a statue, 180/190 A. D.

38 Bust of a man in tunic and cloak (paludamentum), ca. 170 A. D.

39 Lucius Verus, co-regent with Marcus Aurelius (joint reign 161–169 A. D.). Bust in cuirass and cloak (paludamentum)

40 Bust of Lucius Verus in youth, ca. 150 A. D.

41 Relief from large monument with scene from gladiator fight, 1st century B. C.

42 Large floor mosaic from a Roman villa at Sentinum (central Italy), 200/250 A. D.

C. Portraits, two sarcophagi, frieze from the Basilica Ulpia (Rome) in third bay (cf. p. 83, fig. 27)

43 Two portraits of Commodus (Emperor 180–192 A. D.): head and a bust in cuirass and cloak (paludamentum)

44 Head of an old man, 190/200 A. D.

45 Bust of a man, ca. 220 A. D.

46 Statue of a woman (draped statue after Greek prototype of 5th century B. C.), ca. 170 A. D.

47 Bust of a man in tunic and cloak (paludamentum), ca. 200 A. D.

48 Head of a man (fragment), ca. 220 A. D.

49 Septimius Severus (Emperor 193–211). Bust with cuirass and cloak (paludamentum) is ancient but does not belong. 200/210 A. D. (Plate 40)

50 Head of Caracalla as a boy (son of Septimius Severus; Emperor 211–217). 196 A. D.

51 Head of Empress Julia Domna, wife of Septimius Severus. Ca. 195 A. D. (Plate 43)

52 Head of Philip (son of Emperor Philip the Arab), 247–249 A. D.

53 Bust of woman, perhaps Empress Otacilia Severa, wife of Philip the Arab (Emperor 244–249). 240/250 A. D. (Plate 41)

54 Head of a man, perhaps Decius (Emperor 249–251). 240/250 A .D.

55 Head of a man. From a statue, ca. 240 A. D. (Plate 44)

56 Large bust of a man, 220/230 A. D.

57 Head of a man, ca. 260 A. D.

58 Head of a man, 260/270 A. D.

59 Bust of a man, 250/260 A. D.

60 Head of a woman, ca. 260 A. D.

61 Head of a man from bust or statue in armour, 270/290 A. D.

62 Head of a woman, 2nd half of 4th century A. D.

63 Large head of a man, beginning of 4th century A. D. (?)

64 Head of a man, ca. 400 A. D. (Plate 42)

65 Large sarcophagus of a man and wife, ca. 240 A. D.

66 Fragments from large sarcophagus with relief frieze, 250/260 A. D. (Plate 45)

67 Frieze from entablature of Basilica Ulpia in Rome, building dedicated 112 A. D.

ROMAN PORTRAITS

Room XI, at 37 metres the longest room in the building, forms its East side. It was the "Römersaal" or Roman Room of the old Glyptothek before its walls and domes were destroyed in the War.

Now the Roman portraits are assembled here once more. As sculpture alone many of them deserve admiration. They are placed in such a way as to make best use of the light, gently to direct the visitor and to allow him to move about among them freely.

Formerly most of the portrait heads were arranged symmetri- *Pl. 2* cally and by size on shelves against the wall with no regard to their quality or chronological order. Others stood on pairs of tall columns too high up to be viewed comfortably, and many were half hidden in shadow. To appreciate them as living sculpture was not easy in those circumstances. Now the number of busts selected for display has been considerably reduced and these fill the large room in a livelier manner. Yet the old arrangement based on decorative principles was in a sense more correct historically, for the original setting of the portraits was a shrine or niche and the Romans themselves often arranged them against a wall, crowded them together or placed them too high up to see. For them the portraits were not, as they are for us, first and foremost works of art but rather an embodiment in lasting form of their esteem for an individual. They personified the deceased citizen or statesman or general, or they might represent some still living person – a notable, a high official or the Emperor or a member of the Imperial family.

Proof of this rather specialised function of Roman portraits is everywhere to be seen. For one thing the Roman busts are obviously one-sided: The hollowed-out back of the busts was to the wall, and the back of the head was often left incomplete with the hair but lightly chiselled in. Even the three full-length statues of women (2, 25, 46) are flat and one-sided. The direction, so to speak, of the Roman heads was determined by the intensity of the facial expression. Nonetheless they are formed with a real sense of plasticity and movement. Time and again the face and glance are set at an angle, and even the unlifelike scoop of the bust shares in the movement of the head as though it were a part of the living body. The visitor will want to make the most of his opportunity to view the portraits from all sides, historically "incorrect" though this be, as well as of the light which brings them to life.

Roman portraits were for the most part busts, though often only the head is preserved. But there were also portrait statues, of which the body may now be lost. In the case of some heads one can no longer tell to which class they belonged.

The portraits assembled in Room XI take us through half a mil-
lenium of Roman portraiture. The Romans revered their ancestors
and as early as the 2nd century B. C. we hear of the Roman custom
of preserving their likenesses by making death masks which
reproduced "with remarkable fidelity the features" of the deceased. Such was the genesis of Roman portraiture, but by the
1st century B. C. probably leading personalities in Republican
Rome were giving the first impulses to what was to develop over
the centuries as an epoch-making branch of the sculptor's art.
At first it must have been practised exclusively by immigrant
Greek artists who settled in Rome, bringing with them centuries-
long experience of technical skill with the chisel and close obser-
vation of the human face. From the workshops they set up in the
service of Roman patrons came the first unmistakeable Roman
marble portraits. Before long these new lifelike portraits began to
attract a wider section of society and less distinguished citizens
commissioned likenesses of deceased members of the family-
men, women and children alike – to set up in the house, at the
cemetery or even, if the person was much esteemed, in a public
place.

Throughout the development of Roman portraiture as an inde-
pendent art, its centre was always the City of Rome itself. Of the
works displayed in the Glyptothek virtually all are City products.
During the Imperial period the chief impulses for new directions
and variations of style came from the likenesses of deified Emperors and Empresses, their children and other members of the
Imperial house. Mass-produced in innumerable copies and
adaptations, these were distributed both within the City and
throughout the Empire, to be set up everywhere at the State's
behest in temples and sanctuaries and other public buildings
and places.

The characteristically Roman form of portrait is the bust, the head
by itself being seen as sufficient vehicle for the expression of
personality. Here there is a fundamental difference from the
Greek view that a man's being is expressed through the whole
of his form and figure.

The early portraits of the 1st century B. C. terminate in a small
Pls. narrow "scoop" rounded off beneath the collarbones (see so-
35, 34 called "Marius" and young man: 13 and 6). In the course of the
1st and 2nd centuries A. D. the scoop widened out until it

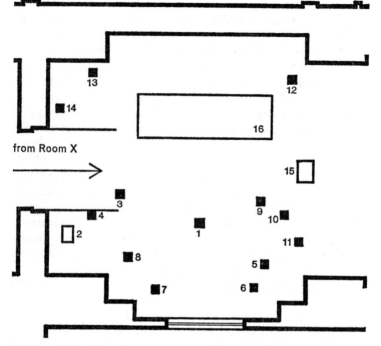

25. Room XI, first bay

reached the shoulders (bust of Augustus: 1) or even included   Pl. 37
them (busts 12 and 19). More and more it came to play a real part   Pl. 38
in the portrait. During the 2nd century it includes the chest muscles and part of the upper arms (Apollodorus and unknown man:
31, 33) or even extends, arms and all, to below the breast ("Ota-   Pl. 39
cilia Severa" and an unknown man: 53, 56). A favourite form from   Pl. 41
the 2nd century onwards had the bust richly draped or in armour
(Antoninus Pius in cuirass and cloak, unknown man in tunic and
cloak, "Otacilia Severa": 32, 38, 53).

The earliest busts (e. g., 13, 6, 12) had no stand, since they were   Pls.
fixed in position in an niche or shrine ("aedicula") or set into herm   34, 35
pillars. (The pillars seldom survive.) It was not until 80/90 A. D.
that busts were made to stand independently on ornamental
cylindrical pedestals. Between this foot and the bust itself was an
elegantly contoured little panel with the person's name inscribed
(Apollodorus: 31) or simply painted on it. The panel, if it has

escaped being removed in recent times, is in many cases broken,
Pl. 39 but on Nos. 31, 33, 38 and 40 it has survived intact. The foot of the
bust is usually missing (complete bust with stand: Antoninus
Pius, 32).

The eyes, lips and hair and certain details on the drapery, armour
and attributes were originally painted (cf. p. 18) but the spectator
must now restore the faded colours in his imagination.

In the three bays of Room XI the portraits are arranged in the
main chronologically.

A. First bay (see fig. 25)
Here we see a century and a half of Roman portrait sculpture,
from the 2nd quarter of the 1st century B. C. to about the end of
the 1st century A. D. There are the *Republican portraits 5–7 and
13–15* (ca. 70–30 B. C.): the statue in armour of an unknown
general (15), the head from a lost statue, draped or in armour,
which may have represented Caius Octavius, the Emperor
Pl. 35 Augustus's father (5), the busts called "Marius" and "Sulla"
made by the sculptor as a pair and certainly representing, if not
Marius and Sulla, two Republican notables whose identity one
would give much to know (13 and 14; the draped bust into which
"Sulla" has been set dates from the Renaissance), and finally
the portraits of two unknown Romans, one young, one elderly
Pl. 34 (bust 6, head 7).

The politically turbulent period of the late Republic is mirrored
in the portraits it produced. Here we meet the true Roman type,
the men to whom the poet Vergil (70–21 B. C.) addressed his
great exhortation "Tu regere imperio populos, Romane, memento!"
("O Roman, remember, rule the nations with thy sway"). This
character is not yet so explicit in the statue of a Roman general (15)
in a cuirass bearing reliefs of a Gorgon-head, a trophy (tree-
trunk with military tunic, helmet, sword and shield) and two
Victories with branch and garland. The general's portrait still
breathes the pathos characteristic of the last expiring stages of
late Greek art, for the sculptor who executed this commission had
not yet grasped the uncorrupted vitality of the Roman manhood
of that time as the sculptors in the new portrait workshops of
Rome were to do so wholeheartedly. We recognise the genuine
Roman of the Republic in the healthy peasant face of "Caius
Octavius" with its fierce, determined glance (5) and in the exalted

excitement and abrupt energetic turn of the head in the brilliantly
chiselled pair called "Marius" and "Sulla" (13 and 14). The same   *Pl. 35*
highly strung yet forceful temperament burns with more subdued
glow in the fine head of a young Roman (6). The masterly portrait   *Pl. 34*
of an elderly man (7) is more sober, filled with an anxious seriousness.

Portraits of the Imperial period (ca. 30 B. C. – 90 A. D.: portraits
1,3, 4, 8–12, torso from a portrait statue *2*). – Head No. 8 from the
early years of Augustus's reign (31 B. C. – 14 A. D.) stands at the
beginning of the period. The detachment and disciplined will-
power so well expressed in it can also be seen in the admirable
portrait of Augustus (1) – posthumous but based on a contempo-   *Pl. 37*
rary likeness of him. But the calm coolness of the portraits from
Augustus's own time has become mild-mannered detachment
in the hands of the later sculptor, who worked in the time of
Claudius (41–54 A. D.; head of Claudius's wife Agrippina, 4) or
Nero (54–68 A. D.). He shows Augustus wearing the "corona
civica" of oak leaves bestowed on him by the Senate in 27 B. C.
for saving the Roman citizenry. "After I had extinguished the
civil wars, and at a time when with universal consent I was in
complete control of affairs, I transferred the Republic from my
own power to the dominion of the Senate and People of Rome.
For this service of mine I was named Augustus (the Latin means
"august, majestic") by decree of the Senate, and the door-posts
of my house were publicly wreathed with bay leaves and a corona
civica fixed over my door and a golden shield was set up in the
Curia Julia (council-building donated by Julius Caesar) which,
as the inscription thereon attests, was given me by the Senate and
People of Rome for my courage, clemency, justice and piety.
After that time I surpassed all in influence . . ." These words from
the first Roman Emperor's official Acts come to mind in this
splendid portrait with its rich and sensuous modelling.

The now headless draped statue (2) is shown by the inscription on the base to have represented Augustus's wife Livia:
AUGUSTAE. IULIAE. DRUSI. F – "(dedicated to) Augusta Julia
daughter of Drusus". It must have been set up after Augustus's
death in 14 A. D., since it was in his will that he made her an official member of his family, the Julii. The bust of a young woman
with a cool, languid air (9) dates from the time of Nero. This court
style gave way to greater animation and realism in the 2nd half of

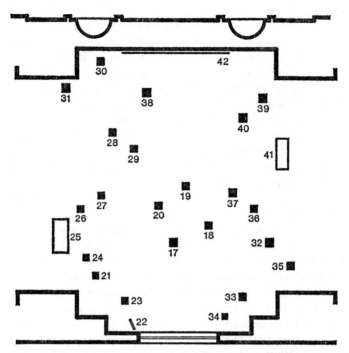

26. Room XI, middle bay

the 1st century, as we see in portraits produced under the Flavian dynasty (69–98 A. D.: Vespasian, Titus, Domitian, Nerva). A good example is the bust of a lady with the high curled "Flavian" coiffure, a virtuoso piece of sculpture (10). The bald-headed priest (11) and bust of a man (12) also belong to this period.

B. Second bay (see fig. 26)
In the middle of Room XI are 2nd-century A. D. portraits from the reigns of Trajan (98–117 A. D.), Hadrian (117–138 A. D.) and the Emperors of the Antonine dynasty (Antoninus Pius, Marcus Aurelius and his co-regent Lucius Verus, and Commodus: 138–192 A. D.). Four of the century's great figures are to be seen portrayed here: Trajan (17), Antoninus Pius (32), Lucius Verus (39 and 40) and Commodus (43 in third bay).
Time of Trajan (ca. 90–120 A. D.: *17–21, 24–27*)
The portrait of Trajan (17) is unique among the portraits of the

Emperors in that no other copy of the type is known. He wears
the "corona civica", the oak-leaf garland granted by the Senate
to all Emperors from Augustus onwards (bust 1 in first bay), with   *Pl. 37*
a medaillion on his forehead set into it. Over his left shoulder is
the aegis with Gorgon-head and snakes symbolising his claim
to rule by divine authority. We know from literary sources that
Trajan's hair was white. Let us then in our imagination restore
the colours to the darkened, weathered marble – green oak-leaves
against the white hair, the medallion perhaps a brilliant gem in
a gold setting, various colours for the garland ribbon, sword-
strap and aegis, red lips, the colours of iris and pupil. Like all the
other busts in the second and third bays, Antoninus Pius's (32)
alone excepted, this bust of Trajan is incomplete. The foot of the
bust and the panel for the inscription are missing (cf. p. 76). The
portrait captures well the austere stubbornness of the man who
renewed Rome's defences through a combination of strict administration and extensive military operations. The simple worthi-
ness and sober deportment of this "best of princes" (Optimus
Princeps), as he was called, became a model for his generation
and is reflected with various nuances in the likenesses of ordinary
citizens. It can be seen in the reserved charm of the little boy (20)
or in the two busts of mature men, the one with stern, hard-lined
features (21), the other with a dry, shrewd expression (19). In the   *Pl. 38*
portrait of a woman (24), found in a grave on the Appian Way
before the City gate and probably hollowed out to receive the
ashes, this new simplicity extends even to the neat, restrained
hair-style. The lady with high diadem and vacuous gaze may be
Trajan's wife Plotina (26). A third woman's portrait with a certain
tired elegance (27) must date from the time of Trajan's accession;
from after his death the statue of a high-born lady (25), no doubt
a member of the Imperial family, shown in the guise of Ceres with
poppy and corn. Finally there is the head of an ivy-garlanded poet
whose artistic pretensions announce themselves characteristically in a weary sentimentality (18).

Time of Hadrian (ca. 120–140 A. D.: *22–23, 29–30, 33*)

A posthumous portrait from a colossal statue of the Emperor
Hadrian (reigned 117–138 A. D.) stands in the museum court-
yard (cf. p. 100). The beautiful fragment of a man's head with
well-kept short beard and thick abundant locks (22) corresponds
exactly to the first portrait made of Hadrian after his accession

in 117 A. D. Cosmopolitan-minded and a passionate philhellene, Hadrian wore his hair and beard after the manner of Greek philosophers. Literary sources tell us that he "took pains over the elegance of his appearance" and that his hair was always "well dressed". His features are large and soft, his expression at once sensuous and cool – what a contrast with his predecessor! And again his manner and appearance were copied by the Roman citizenry.

Pl. 36 We have three portraits from the last decade before Hadrian's death in 138 A. D. T. Caesernius Statianus (29) held high office close to the Emperor and lived to serve his successor, Antoninus Pius. It is from a statue in armour that our excellent head of him comes. No longer do we see the quiet elegance of 20 years before (cf. 22). The glance is uplifted, the flesh more richly modelled to invite play of light and shadow. Moreover we see for the first time two important innovations. Whereas until now the eyes were merely painted (cf. p. 77), from this time onwards they are indicated in the carving, the iris by a ring, the pupil by a little hole. This device, which lends greater intensity to the glance, became a rule to which there are but few exceptions and was further developed as time went on (see portraits of the later 2nd and 3rd centuries). The second innovation is in the hair. By supplementing the chisel with the running drill sculptors now achieved a more virtuoso treatment, loosening up the mass of the hair by means of small drill-holes and thus intensifying the shadow effects in it.

Next to this arresting portrayal of Hadrian's statesman stands the large bust of his favourite Antinous (30). The shallow, effeminate beauty of this Levantine youth from Bithynia epitomises Hadrian's romantic ideal of Hellenism. After his early death he was deified by the Emperor and countless busts and statues of him set up all over the Roman world. Another late Hadrianic work is the superbly finished portrait of an elegant bearded gentleman

Pl. 39 of fashionable society (33). The whole staging of this portrait – the naked bust extending far down, the smartly draped cloak and imposing brooch – make the citizen of the preceding reign

Pl. 38 (19) look plain by comparison.

Antonine period (ca. 140–190 A. D.: *28, 31–32, 34–40*)

Hadrian was succeeded by Antoninus Pius, whose almost undamaged bust (32; the only modern restoration is part of the back of the head) in cuirass and cloak is one of the glories of this collection. He reigned from 138 to 161 A. D. His adoptive son and successor Marcus Aurelius (died 180 A. D. in Vienna) has left us a literary portrait in the famous Stoic "Meditations" he composed in his camp on the Danube: Antoninus was loving and gentle, affable, cheerful and self-sufficient, above flattery and bad taste, hard-working, persevering without being hasty, careful and thorough in forming a judgment and unyielding once he had made it. Even if his appearance were not otherwise known, Marcus Aurelius's circumstantial evaluation of this much respected Emperor would enable us to identify his portrait. It was made ca. 150 A. D.

Marcus Aurelius's co-regent Lucius Verus is represented by two busts (39 and 40; 28 is a bust of Marcus Aurelius's wife, the Empress Faustina, from the Eastern part of the Empire). In the first he is shown in armour as regent (161–169 A. D.). The second, a naked bust probably executed soon after 150 A. D., shows him as a youth of about 22. In this work, outstanding for the quality and good condition of the stone, and in the likewise well preserved draped bust of an unknown man (38) we see at their peak the refined techniques with which the Antonine sculptors handled marble. The frothy curled hair-style then in fashion gave the greatest scope for the manipulation of the running drill, the use of which, as we have seen, was already coming in in the time of Hadrian (see p. 81 on head of T. Caesernius, 29). The chisel *Pl. 36* was now used only for roughing-in (see unfinished parts on back of 38) and the last word now lay not with the tools which gave shape to the stone but with rotating instruments which treated it in a coloristic, pictorial manner, teasing out the chiaroscuro in the luxuriant hair and, by contrast, polishing the skin surfaces to a high lustre, as unweathered portraits show. In portraits like these the plastic qualities of the marble are exploited to the full.

Two portraits stand at the beginning of this period – one, by a sensitive hand, the beautiful head of a priestess with an elaborate hair-style and a garland of ears of grain (34), the other of a man with clouded expression, named on the inscription-panel as Apollodorus (31). Perhaps we may recognise here a posthumous likeness of the architect of that name, a native of Damascus, who worked for Trajan and Hadrian. Hadrian, angered by his criticisms, had him put to death.

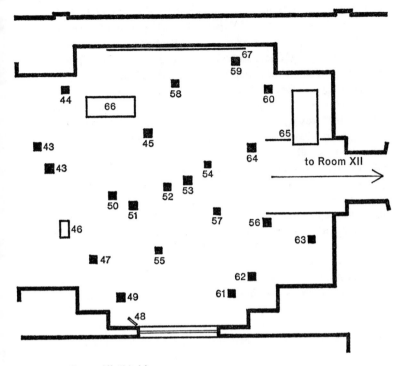

27. Room XI, third bay

From the late Antonine period we have two imposing portraits from the reign of Commodus, the last of the dynasty (180–192 A. D.; two portraits of him in third bay). One, notable for the astoundingly delicate coloristic finish of the surface, is the head, of a soigné gentleman with sparse hair and small beard (37). The other head, that of a curly-headed youthful man (36), achieves by the optical effect of the deepened double boring of the pupils a more direct and compelling gaze than the portraits so far considered.

C. Third bay (see fig. 27)
Most of the portraits here are 3rd-century. Two heads (62 and 63) belong to the 4th century and the latest (64) dates from ca. 400 A. D. Three other portraits belong with the *Antonine period* displayed in the second bay *(43 and 46)*. These are the meticulously

executed draped statue of an unknown Roman lady (46) from
the reign of Marcus Aurelius (161–180 A. D.; cf. contemporary
head of an unknown bearded man, 35 in second section) and two
likenesses (43) of the last Antonine, Marcus Aurelius's degener-
ate son and successor Commodus (180–192 A. D.).

The dignified aristocratic lady (46) with waved hair and a low bun
is clad in fine shimmering drapery copied from a Greek prototype.
Her mantle thrown over her head, she is apparently represented
as a high priestess and so was perhaps of Imperial blood. – The
worthy line of distinguished 2nd-century Emperors breaks off
with the depraved and violent Commodus, who dissipated the
Empire's good government and frontier defences and was finally
assassinated. He is represented here by a head and by a bust
in cuirass and cloak (43). With his death began a century of
bloodshed and misery, an era of short-lived dynasties and a
rapid succession of "soldier Emperors" chosen from, and dependent on, the army.

Portraits from the late 2nd to mid-3rd century A. D. (44–45, 47–56)
"Stand united, make the soldiers rich, never mind about anything
else!" Such was the deathbed admonition of the first soldier-
Emperor, Septimius Severus (193–211 A. D.) to the sons Caracalla and Geta whom he designated joint Emperors. Their joint
rule soon came to an end when Caracalla murdered his younger
brother (reign of Caracalla 211–217 A. D.).

The Glyptothek possesses quite outstanding likenesses of the
African-born Septimius Severus, his wife Julia Domna, who
came from a line of Syrian priest-kings, and their elder son
Caracalla (49–51). Together they form an exotic, dangerously
compelling family picture.

The head of Septimius Severus (49) is the best attested likeness   *Pl. 40*
of him. The bust in cuirass and cloak into which it is now set
does not belong but is ancient. Wishing to legitimise the power
he had taken by force, Severus claimed to be the heir of the
Antonines by adopting himself as son of the great and wise
Marcus Aurelius. To look the part he copied the curly hair-style
and philosopher's beard of the Antonine Emperors. Nonetheless
his shifty, impulsively sentimental expression and the visible
stiffening of the modelling make it plain that the cultured court
life and virtuous Emperors of the previous hundred years are
things of the past (cf. bust of Antoninus Pius, 32 in second bay).

The pathetic sidelong glance to heaven is not that of the Stoic philosopher-Emperor but of the superstitious usurper of god-given rule, a man mixed up, as the historians tell us he was, in magic and astrology.

Pl. 43
Severus's female counterpart can be seen in the wonderful portrait of Julia Domna (51), the Syrian lady whose inscrutable countenance with expressive eyes and mouth is set off by a heavy frame of hair ending in an elaborately plaited coil at the back. The unhappy features of the boy Caracalla (50) are a childish version of the same face. Not only is the family likeness unmistakeable, so also is the official "style" of this foreign dynasty, already at this early age stamped on the boy's character. Nor, finally, can one fail to see in this portrait the future madman, Rome's "second Nero", who was to take delight in causing terror by his very appearance.

To the time of Septimius Severus belong the head (44) and the draped bust in tunic and cloak (47) of two elderly men – curiously disquieting characters, weary and deceitful. Are they perhaps two of the magicians or astrologers the Emperor had about him? The second man was obviously a person of some rank and there is a second, similar, bust of him in the museum store-room. – A less murky cast of mind is reflected in the features of the blasélooking man portrayed in the subtly modelled bust (45). The magnificent and colossal bust (56) shows us a man whose immense physical strength is paired with almost soul-barren energy – an impression added to substantially by the unusually large size of the bust and the metallic shimmer of the close-cropped curly hair and beard. Although he must have been prominent we do not know his name. These two busts were made under the third and the last of the Severans, the Syrians Elagabalus (218–222 A. D.) and Severus Alexander (222–235 A. D.).

Pl. 44
From well on in the first half of the century comes the head from a lost statue (55), a masterpiece in its simple composition, large plain shapes and the spare and graphic rendering of the details in the searching, world-weary face. It is a haunting portrayal of the man with no spiritual home. – The superbly well preserved por-

Pl. 41
trait of a woman (53) gives us a face whose bold-faced brutality is startling. The monumental effect is achieved principally by the structure of the bust and the closed mantle above which the head

rises with such confidence. But the head itself, considered on
its own, seems prim, even almost fragile. Somehow all the deli-
cacy of sculptural treatment and the subtle balances and gra-
dations of feeling which one looks for in a female portrait are
missing. The hair style with its stiff waves and plaited coil at the
back looks as though forged from iron. Perhaps this woman is
Otacilia Severa, wife of the Emperor Philip the Arab (244–249
A. D.). If so, she was also the mother of the boy Philip (Philippus
Minor), whose neighbouring portrait puts before us an uncom-
monly graphic and vivid sharpness of expression in an almost
immobile face (52). This young prince was probably murdered
along with his father at the age of 12. It is interesting to compare
this pair of mother and child with the early Severan pair Julia
Domna and Caracalla (51, 50).   Pl. 43

2nd half of the 3rd century A. D. (57–61) – Seen beside the portraits of Otacilia Severa and Philip the Younger (53, 52) those
from the mid-century and onwards manifest an increasing pre-
occupation with spiritual tensions. In the man's head (54) with
roughly chiselled hair and beard and sharply incised wrinkles –
perhaps the Emperor Decius (249–251 A. D.)? – there is a painful
agitation all the more effective for being combined with the spare
and reserved composition of the face. In a second man's bust (59),
still grandiose despite the damage, it is the enhancement of the
nervous play of tensed, protruding muscles which creates an
unrestrained pathos.

Both outwardly and morally this was the worst era in Rome's
history, an era of which the Bishop Cyprian, martyred in 258 A. D.
in a persecution in Valerian's reign, was to say, "Whatever is
born in these times degenerates in the senility of this world."
In the head of a military leader (61) from an armed bust or statue
the rendering of the beard is even more careless than on the
"Decius" (54), the stereotyped air of pathos even more mechani-
cal and hardened into a crude formula. The art of portrait sculpture was now fast disintegrating, but just before the time of this
portrait there was a last respite under the influence of the Emperor Gallienus (253–268 A. D.). A philhellene, the confidant of
the philosopher Plotinus, Gallienus tried to introduce a new
humanism after the example of Antoninus Pius. The aestheticising
ideal of beauty to which he subscribed is mirrored in the cool
dignity of the small female head (60), whose "helmet" hair-style is

a further development of Otacilia Severa's, and in the portrait
of a bearded man with thick curly hair and smooth face (57).

Three 4th-century portraits (62–64). – A colossal man's head (63),
a woman's head (62) and the very well preserved head of a youth
Pl. 42 (64) afford us a glimpse of this latest century of Roman portrait
sculpture. Fewer portraits were being made now, particularly for
ordinary citizens. The bust too was going out of fashion and it is
colossal statues of the Emperors which typify this period.

Conspicuously as the man's head (63) stands out from the other
two, all three alike exhibit the new monumental concept of the
portrait which sets them apart from the 3rd-century works. From
its great size and imposing style we know that No. 63, made early
in the 4th century, shows us a personage of Imperial rank. Is this
then Constantine the Great (324–337 A. D.) or a member of his
house? Since certain features of this majestic head – the hair
style most obviously – are reminiscent of portraits of the 2nd half
of the 1st century and only to be explained in that light, one won-
ders whether it did not belong, together with others on the same
scale, to some series of "ancestral portraits" of Roman Emperors.

The two "grave and passionless" likenesses, the beautiful wo-
Pl. 42 man's head (62) and the polished head of a youth (64), belong
to a new era. They have shed the burden of what the Greeks called
"physis", the earthly and corporeal life which had been the ceaseless challenge, century by century, of the Roman sculptor. They
"have passed into a transcendental sphere, are composed, as
it were, of crystals, transfigured with light ...", removed from
"their last earthly weightiness, the painful remembrance of an
earlier life-process". From now on it is not sculpture but mosaic
with its mysteriously lit colours which is to transmit the human
and spiritual values of the imminent world of the Byzantine
Middle Ages.

ROMAN RELIEFS

The five reliefs in Room XI cover a long time-span. The friezes
from a rectangular monument found in Rome (16) and the two
blocks from a tomb with gladiator reliefs of large size (41) are
Republican, from the 1st century B. C., the frieze from the Basilica

Ulpia in Rome (67) dates from the reign of Trajan (98–117 A. D.)
and the two relief sarcophagi (65, 66) from the 3rd century A. D.

Large relief monument from Rome, 16 (in first bay) – This relief,
the most extensive we have from Republican times, consists of
two long and two short friezes which join to form an oblong. One
of the long friezes and the two short ones bear a scene from
Greek mythology. These were acquired for Munich by King Ludwig I. On the opposite long side, now in the Louvre, is represented
a Roman public ceremony. Thanks to a cast of these Paris slabs
the friezes can now be seen together for the first time in their
original arrangement. The pilasters at the four corners once
supported a cornice, but this was removed at the time of the monument's discovery and the Munich slabs, originally thicker, sawn
off at the back.

Wedding of Poseidon and Amphitrite, first long frieze and the
two end friezes: in the middle of the long side are Poseidon the
sea-god (Neptune in Latin) and his veiled bride Amphitrite seated   *Pl. 33*
in a chariot drawn by a pair of Tritons with sea-serpent bodies.
One Triton is playing a lyre, the other was blowing into a double
flute, now missing. The chariot, turned halfway towards the
spectator, forms the head of the procession (the frieze as a whole
curves gently outwards towards the middle) along with the bride's
mother Doris, who is enthroned with dignity on a sea-horse to
the left of the Tritons, holding out torches towards the bridal
pair, for the wedding procession of course takes place by night.
From both sides an escort of sea-creatures follows the chariot
as it glides over the water. Riding lazily on a sea-horse and a
sea-cow are the bridesmaids, two Nereids, one on each side.
Little Erotes (Cupids) appear round about, riding, playing, tug-
ging at the bridle. Another pair of Nereids, riding on sea-dragons
and Tritons, brings up the rear on the end slabs. (The incomplete
right-hand frieze with stylistically inadequate marble restorations.)
The background to the scene is the beautiful broad sea. The
calm is broken only by a light breeze and the rush of the sea-
surge. The great awning over Poseidon's chariot hangs like a
slack sail. The Tritons' music is for the winds to hear. And the
swell of the sea can be felt in the splendidly buoyant bodies of the
monstrous, but so friendly, sea-creatures.

The second long side is taken up almost entirely by a scene showing Censors offering sacrifice to Mars. A smaller scene to the

left with only four figures shows the Censors, a pair of high officials in Rome, going about their business, which was to take a census of those eligible to vote, to serve in the army and to pay taxes. We see two seated officials and two citizens. One of the officials is a scribe, busy checking or filling up entries in a register. – The census finished, the Censors make a solemn public sacrifice on the Campus Martius to the war-god Mars, whose youthful armed figure stands by his altar. The sacrificial animals – bull, ram and boar – are led in and amid the throng of musicians, attendants and soldiers the figures of the Censors themselves can be made out – the one by the altar awaiting the procession, the other holding a standard.

The frieze slabs enclosed the massive core of a monument, but what the monument was is not clear. Possibly it was set up by Gellius, one of the Censors of 70 B. C., in the sanctuary of Neptune as a thank-offering for the successful suppression of pirates in the Tyrrhenian Sea.

Gladiator relief, 41 (in second bay) – These two mighty blocks probably came from a Republican grave monument. They form but one part of a larger group of scenes of gladiator fights. Here the victory is being announced by two trumpeters, whose long "tubae" have a valve worked by one finger. The trumpeter in front holds up three fingers – beckoning, perhaps, to the loser, the man on the ground, to exercise his right to beg the spectators for mercy. It is theirs to decide whether he lives or dies. This is the moment just after the duel has ended: the loser waits in suspense while the winner stands by with raised sword in crude readiness to kill him if the audience does not let him off. "The grim event is not without a certain greatness, lent to it by the plain burning truthfulness with which the sculptor has depicted it. No beautiful form, no artful composition, no pretty eloquence. A human being in the face of death conquers through training and habit."

Frieze from the Basilica Ulpia in Rome, 67 (in third bay) – Incense burns on richly ornamented stands while Victory goddesses wreathe the stands with laurel and feed the flames. Sawn out from its architectural setting after its discovery, this was part of a longer decorative frieze with the symmetrical figure-groups continuously repeated, the whole being once topped by a heavy cornice. It belonged to the Basilica Ulpia, a stately public market hall put up by the Emperor Trajan in his forum and dedicated in

28. Roman sarcophagus (Room XI: 66)

112 A. D. Trajan's Forum, now partly excavated, forms with its famous Column and the ruins of the colossal Basilica one of the most admirable sights in Rome.

Two large relief sarcophagi made in Rome in the 3rd century A. D. (65 and 66 in third bay; more Roman sarcophagi in Room XIII, cf. pp. 95 ff.):

Sarcophagus of a man and wife, 65 – This imposing piece was probably made for the burial of both partners, a custom not uncommon in Rome. The couple is portrayed in the centre of the front side, the rest of which is covered with curved ripple ornament. Holding hands, their heads solemnly covered, they are seen in a richly decorated little shrine ("aedicula") with shell-shaped back, pillars and pediment, and sea-Centaurs blowing horns on the roof. The husband is holding a scroll and at their feet stands a little Hymen (spirit of marriage) with a flaming torch. On the corners of the sarcophagus they appear again, this time in idealised form as statues on pedestals – to the right the husband as philosopher holding a scroll, to the left the wife as a Muse, probably Urania with the (now missing) globe of the heavens. – On the ends are crossed shields, battle-axes and lances cut in low relief and left rough. The raw holes were for the clamps which held on a heavy lid. – The hands of the couple, polished smooth from repeated touching, show that the sarcophagus was later re-used in a church and the relief given a Christian interpretation.

Fragments of a sarcophagus with frieze, 66 – Even in its present fragmentary state this sarcophagus demonstrates more conspicuously than that of the married couple (65) the masterly standard in relief art to which the Roman workshops of the 3rd century had attained. It was made for a Roman of high rank, perhaps an Emperor or some member of the Imperial family. What now survives are the two corner pieces from the front with carefully worked and polished high relief, about half of the adjoining narrow end-pieces and one smaller fragment from the middle of the front side.

The front side with its two scenes can be understood with the help of fig. 28, a sketch based on another sarcophagus in Rome. To the left was the dead man in armour and beside him, as personification of his manly courage, the armed goddess Virtus with sword and helmet. In the middle and the right half of the frieze the dead man appeared again, this time as lion-slayer. Attended by companions, he has hunted down a great maned lion and is ready to spear it as it turns towards him (central fragment). On *Pl. 45* the right-hand corner is preserved the earnest, passionate head of a companion who stands back with sword poised ready to strike. A lioness, pierced by a lance, expires at his feet. On the opposite (left) corner a groom leads his master's horse through a gate.

The left-hand end beyond the gate shows in rough low relief the hindquarters of the horse and a squire following after with the general's helmet. On the right-hand end the relief, though not quite finished, is high and well laid out: a second groom, carrying a throwing-stick, hurries by with another horse.

Roman floor mosaic, 42 (in second bay) – This comes from a Roman villa near Sentinum in central Italy, nowadays Sassoferrato in Umbria, and dates from the beginning of the 3rd century A. D. It consists of a central field with picture (ca. 2m. × 2m.), then a wide border of ornamental and architectural motifs (5.25× 5.25) and a strip at the top with a plant pattern.

The picture shows the youthful sun-god Mithras in the circuit of the heavens with the twelve signs of the zodiac between two trees. On the earth reposes the Earth-goddess (Tellus) with the four Seasons as her children. Spring, Summer and Autumn wear garlands of flowers, corn-ears and vine, while Winter lies covered up in his mother's shadow at the root of the tree whose leaves are falling. The other tree, above Spring, bears fresh foliage. "The composition, draughtsmanship and modelling of the figures all proclaim the hand of a master. The ornament in the border undoubtedly ranks with the best of its kind that has come down to us from that period. Its richness and variety of motif are as astounding as is the confident sense of design with which they are put together to form a whole. – The border is not only ornamental, it also performs a spatial function. It is based on the representation in perspective of a series of rising consoles leading from the level of the figure-scene to a visibly higher level. Together with the background the four rows of consoles create the impression of an enclosed space with oblong sides ..." Thus did the villa's original owner enjoy the charm of this optical illusion when he stood on the central field of the mosaic. From the axis of the picture and from the band at the "top", in which symmetrical tendrils untwine from a calyx, it is clear where the main entrance to the room was.

1 Colossal statue of Apollo ("Apollo Barberini"). Free Roman adaptation in 4th-century B. C. style.
2 Statue of Artemis (Diana). Roman work dependent on Greek prototypes. – 1st century A. D.
3 Head of a statue of Herakles (Hercules). Free Roman copy after Greek prototype (330/320 B. C.). – 1st century A. D.
4 Head of Herakles. Copy of a Greek statue (2nd century B. C.)
5 Roman portrait statue (torso). – Copied from a Greek statue of Hermes (4th century B. C.)
6 Head of Hermes. Copy from same prototype as no. 5
7 Heroising statue of Domitian as prince (Emperor 81–96) with sword-belt; once had metal garland in hair. – 70/80 A. D.

This southeast corner room, the round Room XII, has a square Roman floor mosaic let into the middle. Its trick pattern of rows of cubes creates the illusion of three dimensions.

The *colossal statue of Apollo (1)* acquired from the Palazzo Barberini in Rome was discovered in one of the numerous villas belonging to rich Roman families at Tusculum, near present-day Frascati, in the Alban Hills of Latium. Its prototype was probably the cult statue of Apollo, thought by the Romans to be a work of the 4th-century Greek sculptor and architect Scopas, which Augustus set up in the temple of Apollo on the Palatine consecrated after his victory at Actium in 31 B. C. – The archer god, purifier of the world, who shoots down monsters and the sacrilegious, was also to the Greeks the god of music and poetry, leader of the Muses and player of the mighty lyre whose strains symbolised order and measure. Here he is portrayed as Kitharodos, singer to the kithara (a large kind of lyre), clad in festive high-girt tunic and high-soled sandals, a mantle hanging from his shoulders. In his left arm he holds the kithara; its sounding-box is partly preserved. His outstretched right hand probably held a libation-bowl. The missing right arm and left forearm were, like the head, worked separately. With long locks flowing to his shoulders and the curls tied up above his forehead he looks like one of the Muses whose choir he leads. Also, of course, worked separately are the bronze eyelashes and the eyeballs of fine-grained white stone. The iris and pupil of coloured precious stones ("luci di pietra preziosa") were apparently still in place when the statue was discovered.

The *Artemis-Diana (2)*, technically brilliant, is a mannered, eclectic work of Imperial times in which a rigid pose and details (the hair particularly) are curiously combined with the free movement of the fluttering, billowing drapery. In the hollows of the drapery can be seen traces of red colour. The divine huntress held by its fore-paws a fawn which was springing up towards her. The hoofs are still in place in her right hand. The left hand held a bow. The quiver was slung from her right shoulder, its strap, decorated in low relief with an animal frieze (hounds, deer etc.), crossing the breast. On her head she wears an openwork crown with little animal figures (probably stags), over which is thrown a veil.

There are *two heads of Herakles (3 and 4)*. The first, an over-refined bravura piece from Roman Imperial times, is crowned with leaves of poplar, the tree of the underworld, as a reminder that Herakles slew the hell-hound Cerberus at the gate of Hades. The second head (4) is crowned with oak. This large, impassioned head is one of a number of copies of a 2nd-century B. C. statue which showed the hero armed with his club and holding in his outstretched left hand the golden apples of the Hesperides which he had fetched from the dragon-guarded tree at the Western end of the world. The mighty head with its emphatic attitude and thick curly hair belonged to a correspondingly massive body and challenging heroic pose. Another copy of this statue, made in gilded bronze, stood as the colossal cult statue in a round temple of Hercules Victor on the Tiber and is now in the Capitoline Museum in Rome.

A certain *statue of Hermes* by an unknown 4th-century artist was repeatedly copied by the Romans for portrait statues and some-times even set up as such in cemeteries. The copy from which the *torso (5)* comes was evidently adapted to show the deceased Roman as a huntsman, for the copyist has added a support with a dead hare. The original statue, however, showed Hermes in grave and thoughtful attitude as "Psychopompos", escorter of souls to the underworld, according to Greek belief. His left hand, enveloped in his cloak, held the herald's wand which he carried as messenger of the gods. The *head of Hermes (6)* is also copied from this statue.

XIII ROOM OF THE BOY WITH THE GOOSE

A. Sculptures

1 The boy with the goose (250/200 B. C.). Roman copy (Plate 46)
2 Drunken old woman (200/180 B. C.). Roman copy
3 Marsyas, Roman copy from a group (200/190 B. C.)
4 Head of a Satyr (Faun). Roman copy from a statue (ca. 100 B. C.) – 2nd century A. D. (Plate 47)
5 Bronze head of a Satyr (Faun) from a statue, ca. 100 B. C.

B. Roman relief sarcophagi and two small Roman panel reliefs

6 Sarcophagus: death of the Niobids, 160/170 A. D.
7 Sarcophagus: Orestes and Iphigenia, 130/140 A. D.
8 Sarcophagus: Selene and Endymion (front slab), ca. 180 A. D.
9 Sarcophagus: Marriage of Dionysus (Bacchus) and Ariadne (front slab), 150/160 A. D.
10 Sarcophagus: Marriage of Dionysos (Bacchus) and Ariadne, 140/150 A. D.
11 Small sarcophagus of the girl Flaminina (front slab): childhood of Dionysus, ca. 140 A. D.

In small domed room

12 Panel relief: peasant and cow, 1st century A. D.
13 Panel relief: herd of cattle, 1st century A. D.

Roman relief sarcophagi

It was in the reign of Hadrian (117–138 A. D.) that these sarcophagi came into fashion, when the Romans began generally to bury their dead instead of cremating them. Monumental stone coffins came to be used by many sections of Roman society, usually placed in a grave but occasionally standing visible above ground in some sort of tomb structure. They form a branch of Roman art which was to last into Christian times. Mythological scenes such as we see on the sarcophagi from Rome or the nearby harbour town of Ostia displayed here in Room XIII remained in favour until well into the 3rd century. Sometimes the content of a myth was considered as in itself of sufficient worth to adorn a tomb, but in other cases some symbolic connection with the dead seems to have been intended. Thus the story of Dionysus's childhood on the child's sarcophagus (11) promised happiness to the little Roman girl who was buried in it, while adults were offered hope for the afterlife by the marriage of Dionysus and Ariadne (9 and 10) or the love story of the moon-goddess and the sleeping shepherd Endymion (8). Perhaps too the story of Orestes and Iphigenia (7) stands for the unending love of brother and sister.

Sarcophagus (7) with Orestes and Iphigenia depicts the rescue of Orestes and his sister from the barbarous Crimean land of Tauris, a story used by Euripides in the 5th century for his drama "Iphigenia in Tauris" and worked afresh by Goethe. Agamemnon was about to sacrifice his daughter Iphigenia to obtain the gods' blessing for the expedition to Troy. But Artemis, who had a sanctuary among the northern barbarians of Tauris, snatched her away and installed her there as her priestess. Iphigenia's brother Orestes, accompanied by his friend Pylades, comes to Tauris in order to carry away Artemis's cult image and so redeem himself from the curse he incurred by murdering his mother. He discovers his sister and rescues her. – In the centre of the sarcophagus, Orestes and Pylades upon their arrival in Tauris. Orestes is pursued by a Fury (avenging demon) with torch, whip and serpent, while Pylades supports him. To the left the sanctuary with cult image, basin for offerings, sacred tree and temple, upon which hang heads from human sacrifices. Since the barbarians sacrificed all strangers caught in their country to Artemis, one of them is seen bringing Orestes and Pylades before the priestess. To the right the rescue: Iphigenia with the image of Artemis; the fight with the barbarians on the shore; Iphigenia and an attendant on board the ship, Orestes or Pylades leaping aboard. – The ends of the sarcophagus are not quite finished. The left-hand end shows the arrival of Orestes and Pylades (the ship was presumably to be added), the right a barbarian and Iphigenia, who is reading aloud to Orestes and Pylades her secret letter. – The lid is adorned with garlands, Erotes (Cupids), eagles, human heads and dolphins.

Sarcophagus (6) with death of the children of Niobe (cf. dead Niobid Room V: 5, pp. 39 f.): Niobe, mother of seven sons and seven daughters, had taunted the goddess Leto with having only two children. Apollo and Artemis avenged their mother by slaying Niobe's children with their arrows. – Left, Artemis and five of Niobe's daughters with their aged nurse. In the middle the old pedagogue with the youngest son. Right, four more sons and Apollo. – On the left end the other two daughters, on the right end the last two sons with a shying horse (the sons were slain while hunting on Mt. Cithaeron). – On the relief of the lid the dead children, on the left gable the grieving mother.

Sarcophagus (8) tells of the love of the moon-goddess Selene (Luna) for Endymion, the beautiful shepherd on Mt. Latmos who had been granted eternal youth and everlasting sleep. Right, Selene visits the slumbering Endymion while the winged Hypnos (Somnus, Sleep) sprinkles poppy juice from a cornucopia. On the peak sits Latmos, the god of the mountain. – Centre, above: Selene riding on the Crab (Cancer), her sign of the zodiac. – Left, Mother Earth (Tellus), Selene departing from her beloved. Her team is driven by Eos (Aurora, Dawn) and the little Eros (Cupid, Love) accompanies her in multiple form.

Two *sarcophagi (9 and 10)* show the marriage of Dionysus (Bacchus) and Ariadne. No. 10 is complete, of 9 only the front slab remains. Ariadne, the Cretan princess, was abandoned by the Attic prince Theseus on the island of Naxos but later became the immortal bride of the god Dionysus. – On the slab (9), in the shade of a vine the bridal pair in a cart (decorated in relief) drawn by a pair of music-making Centaurs. A Satyr and a little Eros (Love) escort them. In front of the cart drunken Satyrs and Maenads dance and make merry, an aged Silen carries a covered basket on his head. The procession is headed by two Satyrs, one of whom carries the goat-footed Pan on his back while the other whips Pan's backside with a strap. – On No. 10 the bridal cart is drawn by a male and a female Centaur, in the background is a Satyr with a wineskin. In front is a second cart, drawn by panthers, carrying Dionysus's drunken mother Semele. The priestly figure beyond it with torch and libation-bowl may be Demeter. The procession is again led by two Satyrs, who carry the aged Silen. In the winged youths accompanying the two carts we ought perhaps to recognise Hymen, the spirit of Marriage, and in the driver of the panther team Aion, Zeus's charioteer whom he sent to the wedding. On the left end a Satyr with Pan, on the right Pan and a Maenad.

The *child's sarcophagus (11)* bears an incription (above entrance to small domed room), abbreviated and not quite complete, on the upper edge of the relief slab: ... P(osuit). F(iliae) FLAMININA E VIX(it). ANN(o).I.M(ensibus).IIII. D(iebus). VIII. The father had the sarcophagus "set up for his daughter Flaminina. She lived 1 year, 4 months, 8 days". – The frieze depicts the childhood of Dionysus (Bacchus) among the mountain Nymphs and Satyrs (cf. pp. 37f. on statue of Silen, Room V: 2). Nymphs bathe the little child. Right, a Satyr holds him on his hand and the aged Silen holds out a shrub to him. Left, Dionysus rides on a goat, carrying the mystic winnowing-fan over his shoulder, Priapus behind him wrapped in a cloak.

(A seventh sarcophagus, ca. 200 A. D., showing Apollo, Athene and the nine Muses is on display in the East Court of the Antikensammlungen.)

Two panel reliefs

In the small domed room are exhibited two Roman "cabinet pieces", small panels with idyllic rustic scenes depicted in relief. *Panel (12)*, superior to the second panel in its fine execution, shows a bent-backed peasant driving his cow to market. A hare is tied to the stick he carries over his shoulder and a pair of sheep are tied across the back of the cow. Near the stately city gate, through which protrudes the gnarled branch of a plane tree, can be seen a sanctuary of Bacchus with a high, partly ruined, surrounding wall and a low entrance. In the middle of the sanctuary is an elegant tall stand bearing a mystic winnowing-fan with fruit and a phallus. On the wall there are cymbals, torches and an ornamental vase. Above on a rocky eminence stands a small shrine with the pillar-shaped image (herm) of Priapus. The heads of the peasant and the cow, part of the hare etc. are restorations.

Panel (13) shows a herd of cattle in a rocky landscape. Above, near a phallic image of Priapus with a flaming portable altar, sits a mountain god with lion skin and pine branch. Next to him is a dog.

Sculptures

The *bronze head of a Satyr (5)* with pointed ears, wild shock of hair and mocking grimace is a beautifully cast and chiselled piece, the lips being set off by the use of a differently coloured alloy. There were once inlaid eyes of another material (cf. p. 27 on bronze head of a youth, Room III: 7).

Pl. 47   The famous marble "*spotted Faun*" *(4)* is an Imperial work of the highest virtuosity, remarkable for its accurate modelling. The spotting is a later blemish. J. J. Winckelmann saw in this head one "of the most beautiful from antiquity".

The *fettered Marsyas (3)* belongs to a group from Asia Minor known to some extent from copies. Marsyas, a Satyr, had the audacity to compare Apollo's lyre-playing with his own unmelodious noises on the flute. He entered into a contest with the god, and when he lost, Apollo had him flayed alive by a slave. The group showed Marsyas bound hand and foot to a tree while Apollo reposed on a rock with his kithara and the slave, drawing his knife, crouched ready to begin his work. (A 4th-century relief from the workshop of Praxiteles, now in the National Museum, Athens, shows Apollo and the slave listening as Marsyas plays the flute.)

The *drunken old woman (2)*, a marble statue from Smyrna, was attributed by the Romans to a sculptor called Myron. Only the Glyptothek's copy has preserved the head for us. (Restorations on the body are based on a second copy in Rome.) A famous 2nd-century genre piece, as stirring for its artistic quality as for its pitiless realism, it portrays a gaunt old woman clasping in her gnarled hands a full-bellied wine flask with an ivy garland slung round it. Undoubtedly this monumental work was a votive offering at a sanctuary, not a secular work of art in our sense. It was formerly in Mannheim in the collection of the Kurfürst Karl Theodor von der Pfalz.

Pl. 46   The *boy strangling a goose (1)* in over-energetic play (infans amplexando anserem strangulat) was much admired and repeatedly copied by the ancients. Roman tradition names one Boethos as the creator of the original bronze group. The Glyptothek's copy is the best preserved, though it includes a few restorations (head and wing-tips of goose etc.). The original statue may have been set up at a sanctuary of a god of healing as a thank-offering for the recovery of a little boy. (The support is a necessary addition in a marble copy.)

INNER COURT

When the Glyptothek was first built, and again today, the Inner Court was open and connected to the Entrance Hall by a tall glazed doorway. But as early as 1864, only 34 years after the opening of the museum, the Court had to be sacrificed – by the original architect himself, Leo von Klenze – in order to accommodate a structure to house newly acquired reliefs from Assyria. At the same time the central portion of the façade overlooking the Court was covered over and the glazed doorway walled up and replaced by a narrow entrance passage leading to the new room. The Assyrian Room was not rebuilt after the War. The reliefs are now housed with the Egyptian collection in the Residenz.

The rebuilding after the War provided an opportunity for some improvements. The floor of the Court was raised by 1 m. and the blank walls of the rooms, previously broken only by the half-moon windows (lunettes), opened up by the insertion of large windows. By this means both the Court and the interior of the building have benefited. The exhibition rooms, which were poorly lit before, now receive ample daylight, while the Court no longer looks empty and forbidding. In addition the two have been brought into a living relationship which is architecturally more satisfying.

The large column of Untersberg marble displayed in the Inner Court comes from the earlier Entrance Hall of Friedrich von Ziebland's neoclassic museum building which faces the Glyptothek from the South side of the Königsplatz. This is the building which has since 1967 housed the Antikensammlungen (cf. p. 4). Gutted in the War, it has been rebuilt inside in modern style.

In the centre of the Court can be seen a large bronze head of the Emperor Hadrian. This is an outstanding modern cast of an ancient marble head found at the beginning of the 18th century in the Emperor's great mausoleum in Rome, the famous Castel Sant' Angelo. Now in the Vatican Museums, it probably belonged to a statue which stood in the open air by the mausoleum. Of the many surviving portraits of Hadrian this is the most imposing and monumental.

The inscription on the 18th-century marble base refers to the "Greek work dug up on the Esquiline Hill to the benefit of the arts" (Graecum opus artium bono effossum Esquiliis) which once stood upon it. This was a Roman copy of the renowned "Discus-thrower" (Discobolus) by the classical Greek sculptor Myron, an influential masterpiece admired from antiquity to the present day. The Esquiline Discobolos belonged to the Glyptothek from 1938 until it was reclaimed by Italy ten years later. It now stands in the Museo Nazionale delle Terme in Rome.

SOME NOTES ABOUT THE GLYPTOTHEK

History and description of the building

1804–05 Crown Prince Ludwig makes his first journey to Italy, 1804, starts his collection and expresses the wish to found a museum of ancient sculpture.

1808 Competition for plans for additions to the city, now a royal residence (Bavaria became a Kingdom, 1806).

1809–10 Plans by the architect Karl von Fischer for two buildings on the Königsplatz, one of which was probably intended for a sculpture museum.

1812 Roughly laid out Königsplatz recorded on map of city.

1813 Crown Prince Ludwig proposes a competition "for a building intended for the exhibition of plastic works" (letter of 27 March 1813 to architect Karl Haller von Hallerstein, on whom see p. 55).

1814–16 Royal Bavarian Academy of the Fine Arts (Königliche Bayerische Akademie der Bildenden Künste) commissioned by Ludwig, 1814, with launching a prize competition. Deadline finally fixed for 1 January 1816. The architects Fischer, Haller von Hallerstein and Leo von Klenze submit designs which however do not satisfy Ludwig.

1816 Fischer and Klenze submit new plans at the beginning of the year. Klenze's design is approved by Ludwig and he works out final plans.

Foundation stone of museum laid on 23 April.

The name "Glyptothek" occurs for first time in Ludwig's letter of 12 April to Haller von Hallerstein: ". . . the Glyptothek, for that is what I call the building which is to house the works of ancient and modern sculpture." It is a new word, formed on analogy with Greek words such as "pinakotheke" and "bibliotheke" ("glyptic" meaning art of carving metal or stone). Later the same name is to be adopted for the collection of antiquities in Copenhagen, the Ny Carlsberg Glyptotek.

1820 Basis structure finished.

1821 Columned porch facing Königsplatz begun.

1828 Evening festivities in the Glyptothek.

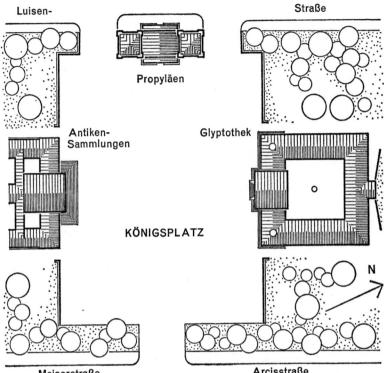

Luisen-   Straße

Propyläen

Antiken-   Glyptothek
Sammlungen

KÖNIGSPLATZ   N

Meiserstraße   Arcisstraße

29. Königsplatz with Glyptothek and Antikensammlungen

1830	Building completed, summer 1830. Klenze writes to King Ludwig, 30 September: "Your Majesty was pleased to command that the Glyptothek be finished by the 1st of October. It is, and Your Majesty will find the key enclosed." The Glyptothek is "opened for the people" by King Ludwig without official ceremonies.
1864	Klenze on the King's orders builds a special hall in the Inner Court for the newly acquired Assyrian reliefs. The tall glazed door is walled up and replaced by a passage leading to the Assyrian Room (cf. p. 100).
1935	Königsplatz paved. The pavement, still in place at the present day, raises the level of the square so that the Glyptothek's façade and front steps now lie one step underground. Originally the square had been divided

into four lawns and planned as a cul-de-sac for re-
creation on the edge of the city, opening towards the
Briennerstraße and closed by the Propylaea. Today it is
cut across by two roadways and used as a car park.

1939   Glyptothek closed at beginning of War.

1944   Shells destroy some 40% of the building. Roofwork
        burns, Room I and XI collapse.

1947–53 Temporary reconstruction of all Rooms but XI. (Assyr-
        ian Room in Inner Court not to be rebuilt.)

1956   Bare brickwork structure of Room XI rebuilt.

1957–61 Discussion of plans for interior reconstruction of ex-
        hibition Rooms, the War and its consequences having
        destroyed 90% of the sumptuous and colourful deco-
        ration (marble floors, stuccoed walls, painted stucco
        decoration in domes, frescoes by Peter von Cornelius in
        former reception Rooms VII–IX). At a conference of the
        museum authorities in 1957 H. Diepolder, Director of the
        collections, suggests that only Rooms I and XIII be
        restored to their original form, Room XI, the largest, be
        provided with overhead lighting and a door on to the Inner
        Court, in the other Rooms the basic structure with its
        architectural elements simply be plastered. Others de-
        mand complete restoration of original rich decor of all
        Rooms, Cornelius' ruined frescoes included; further,
        that a modern annexe be built on to the completely
        restored Glyptothek to house the sculptures, or alter-
        natively a modern pavillion in the Inner Court or whole
        Court to be glazed over. Certain compromise solutions
        having been partly tried out, J. Wiedemann speaks out
        against them and proposes that instead of restoration
        the old brickwork of the walls and ceilings alone be
        conserved and covered simply with a thin plaster coat-
        ing (1961).

1962   A similar plan is proposed by the author on 15 February
        at a meeting of the Bavarian Architecture Committee
        (Landesbaukunstausschuß): the basic conception of
        Klenze's halls to be kept, no compromises over deco-
        ration. With the co-operation of H. Syndikus he submits
        this proposal: "In such rooms as these – good in them-
        selves, quiet and exceptionally light – our antiquities can

find a truly worthy home, if only some way can be found to give the brickwork of Klenze's walls a suitable surface with altering their original structure. Klenze's Glyptothek would be able once more, and indeed better than ever, ... to fulfil its function ... as a living museum and one with a great future before it."

1964–71 After abortive attempts J. Wiedemann is entrusted with the planning (1964) and execution (1967) of the restoration of the interior according to his suggestion: the structure is put in order, the walls, whether preserved intact or rebuilt as originally, given an unobtrusive plaster coating and the floor throughout the building paved with shell-limestone slabs. – Level of Inner Court is raised and windows made in the previously poorly-lit Rooms which overlook it (I, III–V, VII–IX, XI, XIII).

1971–72 Artificial lighting installed for evening opening (proposed and carried out by the museum authorities).

1972 Re-opening of the Glyptothek, 28 April.

Exterior of the building (Pl. 1)

Portico with two rows of Ionic columns, crowned by a pediment. Pediment group designed by Johann Martin von Wagner (cf. p. 56): Athene as patron of the plastic arts, which are represented by eight figures (sculptor, founder, wood-carver etc.). Along main front, on each side of portico, three niches with statues of mythical and historical representatives of the arts, from right to left: Daedalus, Prometheus, Hadrian, Pericles (destroyed in War), Phidias, Hephaestus. On the East and West sides of the building six niches each, with Renaissance and modern sculptors: first among the latter on the East side are Canova and Thorvaldsen (two of the original statues on this side were destroyed).

Original arrangement of the Rooms and Crown Prince Ludwig's conception of the museum

The collection of Greek and Roman sculpture was housed in Rooms II–VI and X–XII (II–VI and IX–XI according to the original numbering), while Room I was set aside for selected works of Egyptian art in order, as Klenze says in the first "Description of the Glyptothek of H. M. King Ludwig I of Bavaria" (Beschreibung der Glyptothek Sr. Majestät des Königs Ludwigs I. von Bayern,

Munich, 1830), "to demonstrate the foundations upon which Greek sculpture rests". (The Egyptian sculptures and the Assyrian reliefs were transferred in 1971 to the Egyptian Collection in the Residenz). The series culminated in the "Room of the Moderns" (XIII, originally numbered XII), where stood works by "modern", chiefly classicistic, masters, including busts and statues by Canova and Thorvaldsen. (All these went in 1919 to the Neue Pinakothek.) Of the present-day Aegina Rooms (VII–IX) on the building's North side Klenze says in his "Description", "To make provision for evening assemblies among the statues by torch-light, some rooms were necessary which should contain no ancient sculptures. These the architect thought it fitting to place at the centre of the collection...". The two large reception rooms VII and IX (VII and VIII by the old numbering) together with the smaller vestibule between them (now Room VIII but originally called "the Small Lobby"), which has a small columned porch and ramp on its outward side, served for these royal soirées. A kitchen annexe which Ludwig planned was never constructed.

In the Glyptothek, which was the first public art museum of the city of Munich, the role of the exhibits stood in very strict, and sometimes subordinate, relation to the architecture. They were arranged symmetrically and according to the axis of the room, fixed to the wall or a niche, placed high up against the wall or on a tall pedestal and disposed according to a purely decorative scheme without regard to the lighting. As for new acquisitions of Roman busts, it remained to be seen, so King Ludwig wrote, whether they should be set up on pedestals "as decoration" or "in long rows, even if only on the dark side" of the room.

"The arrangement as a whole produced in the event a truly imposing sequence of halls, though the individual works were, to be sure, robbed of their full effect, which was more or less ignored for the sake of the decorative whole" (Hans Diepolder). The Glyptothek, however, was conceived as a kind of Hall of Fame of ancient sculpture and its fixed and selective display had the purpose of giving expression to a novel and unique idea on the part of its royal founder. It was, in Klenze's words, intended "to impart to the beholder an idea of the regard paid by modern art to these antique masterpieces and to make him forget the uncomely condition in which centuries of barbarism and destruction have so often brought them down to us". It was thus the embodiment of a veneration of the "relics" of ancient art which was both deeply felt and of educational intent. Like a sumptuous gold setting around a worn precious gem, the halls of the Glyptothek, brilliant in their royal splendour, were a worthy home for the venerable monuments of antiquity *(Pl. 2)*.

When the Glyptothek was rounded off in 1830, it was of necessity an unalterable whole. The complete unity of building and contents permitted of no growth or change in the collection. When later the acquisition of new works made it necessary to do away with the reception rooms (they were used for display from about 1875) and to remove the "moderns" (in 1919), these were more than superficial changes. Nor indeed were the admission, still earlier, of non-classical works from the Near East (in 1864) and the building of the Assyrian Room in the Inner Court to accommodate them. The original form of the Glyptothek and its classicistic raison d'être as a "pillar of art education" to open up new paths to the plastic arts and form a new generation of sculptors had been dealt a mortal blow.

PROVENANCES AND SOURCES OF WORKS EXHIBITED

(F = find-place; Pal. = Palazzo; date in parentheses = year acquired)

Room I
1 F Attica (1909)
2 F near Corinth (1853)
3 Rome (1892)
4 Museum für Völkerkunde, Munich (1896)
5 F probably Paros (1821)
6 F Rhamnous in Attica, sancturay of Nemesis (1853)
7 Athens, Parthenon
8 Athens, Erechtheum
9 Bassae in Arcadia, temple of Apollo

Room II
1 F Rome, Castel Sant'Angelo = mausoleum of Hadrian (1813)
2 Rome, Pal. Rondanini (1811)
3 Greece (1882)
4 Antiquarium in Munich Residenz
5 Greece (1878)
6 Neue Pinakothek (1898)

Room III
1 Rome, Villa Albani (1815)
2 Rome, Villa Albani (1815)
3 Rome (ca. 1810)
4 Rome, Villa Ridolfi (1812)
5 (1939)
6 F South Italy (1926)
7 F South Italy; Rome, Villa Albani (1815)
8 Rome
9 Rome, Pal. Braschi (1812)
10 Rome (1821)
11 F Rome (1918)
12 Venice, Pal. Giustiniani-Recanati (1900)
13 Rome, Pal. Barberini (1814)
14 Verona, Pal. Bevilacqua (1811)
15 F Tusculum = Frascati near Rome, Villa Albani (1816)

Room IV
1 F Attica (1910)
2 F Attica (1910 and 1913)
3 F Attica (1913)

4 Antiquarium in Munich Residenz (1921)
5 Rome (1906)
6 F Athens (1899)
7 F Athens (1908)
8 F Panderma near Cyzicus, Sea of Marmara (1925)
9 (1911)
10 Greece (1939)
11 Greece
12 Greece

Room V
1 Rome, Villa Albani (1816)
2 Rome, Pal. Gaetani, later Pal. Ruspoli (1812)
3 Rome (1811)
4 Rome; later Prague, collection of Emperor Rudolph II (1814)
5 Rome, Casa Maffei; later Verona, Pal. Bevilacqua (1811)
6 Rome (1815)
7 Athens (1912)
8 –
9 F Fiumicino near Rome; Rome, Pal. Braschi (1811)
10 Rome (1939)
11 Rome (1900)
12 (with head) Rome, later Pal. Ruspoli (1812) (torso) Rome, Pal.Gaetani,later Pal. Ruspoli (1811)
13 Rome, in possession of J. J. Winckelmann, later Villa Albani (1815)
14 F Ostia near Rome (1809)
15 –
16 Rome (1900)
17 Rome, Pal. Braschi (1812)

Room VI
1 (1906)
2 Greece (1912)
3 Greece (1912)
4 Greece (1939)
5 South Italy (1912)
6 (1878)

7 F South coast of Asia Minor (1906)
8 –
9 F Athens (1811)
10 Greece (1912)
11 Greece (1912)
12 (1907)
13 Rome (1900)

Rooms VII–IX
   F Aegina, sanctuary of Aphaea (1812)

Room X
1 Rome, Pal. Rondanini (1814)
2 F Rome, Circus of Maxentius (1828)
3 Rome, Pal. Rondanini (1810)
4 (1966)
5 F Erythrae in Asia Minor (1920)
6 Antiquarium in Munich Residenz (1920)
7 Antiquarium in Munich Residenz (1920)
8 Apollonia on the Rhyndacus, Asia Minor (1911)
9 F Cumae, South Italy (1821)
10 Rome (1811)
11 Venice, Pal. Giustiniani-Recanati (1900)
12 Antiquarium in Munich Residenz (1920)

Room XI
1 Verona, Pal. Bevilacqua (1815)
2 F Falerone near Rome; Rome, Pal. Braschi (1820)
3 Verona, Pal. Bevilacqua (1811)
4 –
5 (1970)
6 Rome (1821)
7 Verona, Pal. Bevilacqua (1811)
8 Rome, Pal. Rondanini (1811)
9 –
19 Rome, Pal. Rondanini (1811)
11 –
12 –
13 Rome, Pal. Barberini (1814)
14 Rome, Casa Crescenzi, later Pal. Gaetani and Pal. Ruspoli (1814)
15 F Tusculum = Frascati near Rome (1930)
16 Rome, Pal. Santa Croce (1816)
17 Verona, Pal. Bevilacqua (1811)
18 Rome (1822)
19 F Ostia near Rome (1809)
20 (1917)
21 Verona, Pal. Bevilacqua
22 Rome (1822)
23 Rome (1820)
24 F Rome, Via Appia (1816)
25 Rome, Pal. Braschi (1820)
26 Rome (1820)
27 Rome (1816)
28 (1968)
29 (1968)
30 Verona, Pal. Bevilacqua (1811)
31 Rome (1820)
32 Rome, Casa Crescenzi, later Pal. Gaetani and Pal. Ruspoli (1811)
33 Rome (1814)
34 Rome (1828)
35 –
36 –
37 (1811)
38 Verona, Pal. Bevilacqua (1811)
39 Verona, Pal. Bevilacqua
40 Rome, Villa Albani (1815)
41 F Rome (1899)
42 F Sentinum = Sassoferrato, central Italy (1828)
43 (head) Rome, Villa Albani (1815)
43 (bust) Verona, Pal. Bevilacqua
44 Rome, Pal. Ruspoli (1811)
45 Rome (1811)
46 Verona, Pal. Bevilacqua (1814)
47 Verona, Pal. Bevilacqua
48 Munich, Lenbachhaus (1967)
49 Verona, Pal. Bevilacqua
50 (1815)
51 F Porcigliano; Rome, Pal. Chigi (1816)
52 –
53 (1816)
54 Munich, Lenbachhaus (1967)
55 –
56 Verona, Pal. Bevilacqua (1815)
57 Pompeianum, Aschaffenburg (1971)
58 Rome
59 Rome (1824)
60 Rome (1816)
61 –
62 Rome (1822)
63 Rome (1839)
64 Rome (1821)
65 (1967)

66 (1969, 1971)
67 F Rome, Basilica Ulpia in Trajan's Forum, Pal. della Valle (1816)

Room XII
1 F Tusculum; Rome, Pal. Barberini (1815)
2 F Gabii near Rome (1811)
3 –
4 Rome (1897)
5 Frascati, Villa Aldobrandini (1811)
6 F Capua, South Italy (1821)
7 F Labicum near Rome; Villa Albani (1815)
– (Mosaic) –

Room XIII
1 Rome, Pal. Braschi (1812)
2 Rome; collection of Kurfürst Johann Wilhelm von der Pfalz, later Mannheim and Antiquarium in Munich Residenz (1895)
3 F Rome
4 F Rome, Via Appia; Villa Albani (1816)
5 Rome, Villa Albani (1815)
6 F Rome, Via Appia (1828)
7 Rome, Pal. Accoramboni, later Villa Ridolfi (1817)
8 F Ostia (1826)
9 F Ostia (1826)
10 Rome, Pal. Braschi (1812)
11 Rome, Villa Albani (1815)
12 F Rome (1858)
13 Rome, Pal. Rondanini (1814)

Inner Court
Rome, Pal. Barberini (modern cast; original F Rome, Castel Sant'Angelo = mausoleum of Hadrian) (1815)

CONCORDANCE

Abbreviations:

FW = A. Furtwängler, Beschreibung der Glyptothek König Ludwigs I.
zu München, 2. Aufl., besorgt von P. Wolters. Munich, 1910
W = P. Wolters, Führer durch die Glyptothek König Ludwigs 1. zu
München. Munich, 1935
AS = Inventory of Munich Antikensammlungen
E = acquisitions since 1965
DV = Special List (Durchgangsverzeichnis)

Exhibition Number	FW	W. E. AS. DV	Exhibition Number	FW	W. E. AS. DV
Room I: 1		W 169	IV: 9		W 473
I: 2	47	W 168	IV: 10		W 498
I: 3	273	W 273	IV: 11		DV 33
I: 4	48	W 170	IV: 12		DV 32
I: 5	241	W 241	Room V: 1	219	W 219
I: 6	198	W 198	V: 2	238	W 238
I: 7	195	W A 230	V: 3	302	W 302
I: 8	242	W 242	V: 4	270	W 270
I: 9	243	W 243	V: 5	269	W 269
Room II: 1	218	W 218	V: 6	272	W 272
II: 2	252	W 252	V: 7		W 480
II: 3	206	W 206	V: 8	246	W 246
II: 4	52	W 174	V: 9	258	W 258
II: 5	456	W 456	V: 10	257a	W 479
II: 6	329	W 329	V: 11	250a	W 477
Room III: 1	304	W 304	V: 12	228	W 228
III: 2	295	W 295	V: 12	229	W 229
III: 3	265	W 265	V: 13	261	W 261
III: 4	247	W 247	V: 14	210	W 210
III: 5	271b	W 484	V: 15	204	W 204
III: 6		W 523	V: 16	249a	W 476
III: 7	457	W 457	V: 17	227	W 227
III: 8	56	W 179	Room VI: 1	272b	W 492
III: 9	212	W 212	VI: 2		W 497
III: 10	294	W 294	VI: 3		W 493
III: 11		W 519	VI: 4	271c	W 485
III: 12	248a	W 475	VI: 5		W 481
III: 13	208	W 208	VI: 6		AS 10.078
III: 14	236	W 236	VI: 7	271a	W 482
III: 15	213	W 213	VI: 8		DV 34
Room IV: 1		W 491	VI: 9	209	W 209
IV: 2		W 495/496	VI: 10		W 486
IV: 3		W 487	VI: 11		W 489
IV: 4		W 520	VI: 12		W 512
IV: 5	272a	W 490	VI: 13	252a	W 478
IV: 6	199	W 199	Room X: 1	298	W 298
IV: 7	271d	W 483	X: 2	292	W 292
IV: 8		W 522			

Exhibition Number	FW	W. E. AS. DV	Exhibition Number	FW	W. E. AS. DV
X: 3	303	W 303	XI: 43	358	W 358
X: 4		E 532	XI: 43	385	W 385
X: 5		W 509	XI: 44	429	W 429
X: 6		W 511	XI: 45	396	W 396
X: 7		W 507	XI: 46	427	W 427
X: 8		AS 10.067	XI: 47	382	W 382
X: 9	234	W 234	XI: 48		DV 35
X: 10	266	W 266	XI: 49	357	W 357
X: 11	213a	W 472	XI: 50	352	W 352
X: 12		W 510	XI: 51	354	W 354
Room XI: 1	317	W 317	XI: 52	360	W 360
XI: 2	367	W 367	XI: 53	356	W 356
XI: 3	314	W 314	XI: 54		DV 36
XI: 4	316	W 316	XI: 55	362	W 362
XI: 5		E 537	XI: 56	384	W 384
XI: 6	413	W 413	XI: 57		DV 46
XI: 7	320	W 320	XI: 58	275	W 275
XI: 8	323	W 323	XI: 59	386	W 386
XI: 9	351	W 351	XI: 60	355	W 355
XI: 10	333	W 333	XI: 61	381	W 381
XI: 11	423	W 423	XI: 62	406	W 406
XI: 12	420	W 420	XI: 63	417	W 417
XI: 13	319	W 319	XI: 64	379	W 379
XI: 14	309	W 309	XI: 65		E 533
XI: 15		W 527	XI: 66		E 536
XI: 16	239	W 239	XI: 66		E 538
XI: 17	335	W 335	XI: 67	348	W 348
XI: 18	343	W 343	Room XII: 1	211	W 211
XI: 19	414	W 414	XII: 2	214	W 214
XI: 20		W 505	XII: 3	271	W 271
XI: 21	415	W 415	XII: 4	245	W 245
XI: 22	285	W 285	XII: 5	290	W 290
XI: 23	341	W 341	XII: 6	289	W 289
XI: 24	342	W 342	XII: 7	394	W 394
XI: 25	377	W 377	XII	vor 441	W 503
XI: 26	405	W 405	Room XIII: 1	268	W 268
XI: 27	398	W 398	XIII: 2	437	W 437
XI: 28		E 535	XIII: 3	280	W 280
XI: 29		E 534	XIII: 4	222	W 222
XI: 30	400	W 400	XIII: 5	450	W 450
XI: 31	334	W 334	XIII: 6	345	W 345
XI: 32	337	W 337	XIII: 7	363	W 363
XI: 33	402	W 402	XIII: 8	328	W 328
XI: 34	410	W 410	XIII: 9	365	W 365
XI: 35	404	W 404	XIII: 10	223	W 223
XI: 36	344	W 344	XIII: 11	240	W 240
XI: 37	332	W 332	XIII: 12	455	W 455
XI: 38	339	W 339	XIII: 13	251	W 251
XI: 39	375	W 375	Front Hall	206a	W 471
XI: 40	340	W 340	Inner Court	278	W 278
XI: 41	364	W 364			
XI: 42		W 504			

Thanks are due to Klaus Vierneisel and Martha Ohly for assistance of many kinds in the preparation of the text.

Text figures nos. 1, 2, 8, 12–14, 16, 18–21, 23, 25–29 drawn by Ernst-Ludwig Schwandner, nos. 3–7, 9–11, 17, 22, 24 drawn by Renate Dolz.

Plates: Fotos of Staatliche Antikensammlungen und Glyptothek. Taken by Franz Kaufmann (Plates 1–2, 8–9, 18, 20, 22–25, 27–29, 32, 37), Hartwig Koppermann (Plates 3, 5–7, 10–17, 19, 21, 26, 30–31, 33–36, 38–48), Eva-Maria Stresow-Czakó (Plate 4).

Quotations

p 17 *Early Greek kouroi – what a great* ... *(Frühgriechische Jünglinge: ein großes* ...*) –* E. Buschor, Frühgriechische Jünglinge

p. 18 *No portion of a figure's surface* ... *(Kein Stück der Oberfläche* ...*) –* H. von Hofmannsthal, Buch der Freunde

p. 18 *Sovereign Founder ("Es ist Homer, der dichter fürst und ahn")* – St. George, Dante, Göttliche Komödie, Übertragungen (4. Aufl.): Dante, Divine Comedy: Hell, canto IV, v. 88 *(Quelli e Omero, poeta sovrano)*

p. 20 *One seems to hear* ... *(glaubt man, ihn tief* ...*) –* H. Meyer, Beilage I zu J. J. Winckelmanns sämtliche Werke, Einzige vollständige Ausgabe, von J. Eiselein, Donaueschingen 1825, vol. 4

pp. 20 f. *one of the greatest* ... *(einer der größten der Antike,* ...*) –* E. Buschor, Die Plastik der Griechen (1958)

p. 22 *work of art which belongs* ... *(einer mythischen Urzeit* ... *) –* Goethe, letter to Ludwig I of Bavaria thanking him for sending a plaster cast of the Medusa, 1825

p. 22 *marvellous work* ... *(wundersamen Werk,* ...*) –* Goethe, Italienische Reise (Rome, 14 April 1788)

p. 22 *face of exalted beauty* ... *(hohen und schönen Gesichtsform) –* Goethe, Italienische Reise (Rome, 25 December 1786)

p. 22 *indescribable and inimitable* ... *(unaussprechlichen und unnachahmlichen* ...*) – Goethe*, Italienische Reise (Rome, 29 July 1787)

p. 28 *Of all her many statues,* ... *(Die von der Poesie der Griechen* ...*) –* A. Furtwängler, Beschreibung der Glyptothek König Ludwigs I. (2. Aufl., besorgt von P. Wolters), on no. 213

p. 31 *The grave monuments are affectionate* ... *(Die Grabmäler sind herzlich* ...*) –* Goethe, Italienische Reise (Verona, 16 September 1786)

p. 75 *with remarkable fidelity* ... – Polybius VI, 53, 5

p. 87 *grave and passionless (leidlos ernst) –* P. Yorck von Wartenburg, Italienisches Reisetagebuch

p. 87 *have passed into a transcendental sphere,* ... *(sind in eine übersinnliche Sphäre* ...*) –* E. Buschor, Die Plastik der Griechen (1958)

p. 89 *The grim event* ... *(Der grausige Vorgang* ...*) –* C. Weickert, Gladiatorenrelief der Münchner Glyptothek, Münchner Jahrb. d. bild. Kunst, N. F. 2, 1925

p. 91 *The composition, draughtsmanship* ... *(Komposition wie Zeichnung* ...*) –* G. J. Kern, Das Jahreszeiten-Mosaik von Sentinum und die Skenographie bei Vitruv, Jahrb. d. Deutschen Archäol. Instituts 53, 1938

p. 99 *of the most beautiful from antiquity (der schönsten aus dem Altertume) –* J. J. Winckelmann, Geschichte der Kunst des Altertums (Phaidon-Verlag 1934, 158)

p. 106 f. *The arrangement as a whole* ... *(Die mit erlesenem Geschmack* ...*) –* H. Diepolder, Antikensammlungen München, in Bayer. Kulturpflege, Beiträge zur Geschichte der Schönen Künste in Bayern

PLATES

1 Glyptothek, façade on the Königsplatz (before 1939)

2   Glyptothek. Room of Roman Portraits (XI) before its destruction in the war

3 Glyptothek. Room of Eirene (V)

4   Portrait of Homer, 460/450 B.C. (copy). Ht. 40 cm. Room I: 3

5   Head of the Kouros of Tenea, 560/550 B.C. Ht. of detail 33 cm. Room I : 2

6 Statue of Diomedes, ca. 430 B.C. (copy). Ht. 102 cm. Room III : 1

7 Attic kouros (youth), 540/530 B.C. Ht. 211 cm. Room I : 1

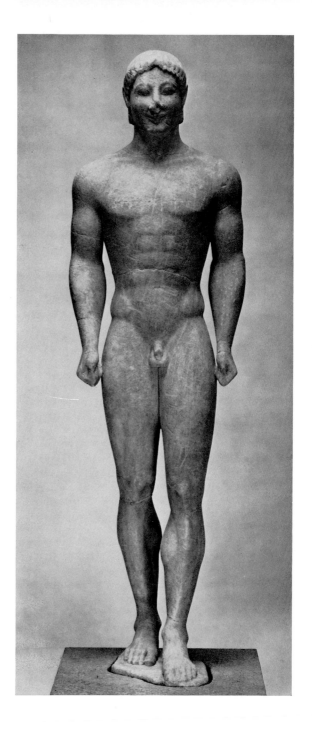

8 Moulding from the Erechtheum, Acropolis of Athens (detail), ca. 410 B.C.
Ht. 52 cm. Room I : 8

9 ‹Barberini Faun›, ca. 220 B.C. Ht. of detail 44 cm. Room II : 1

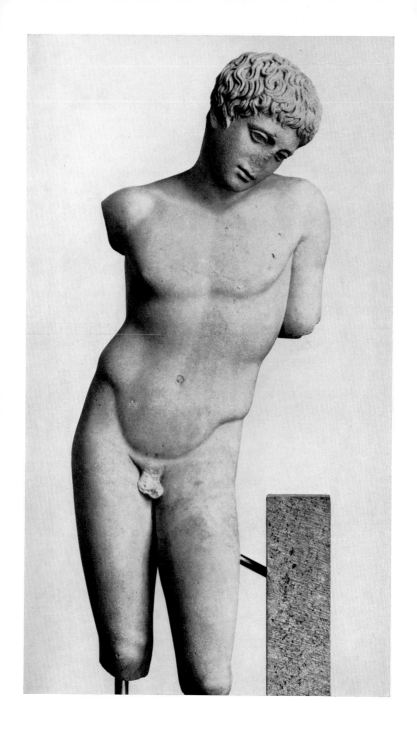

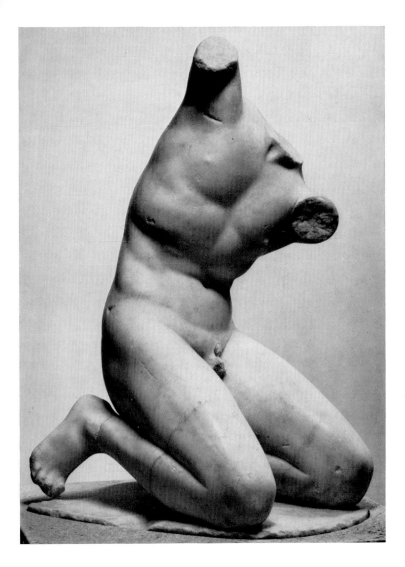

11   Torso of kneeling youth, ca. 300 B.C. Ht. 89 cm. Room V : 4

10   Statue of a boy, ca. 410 B.C. (copy). Ht. 83 cm. Room III : 5

12   Head of Aphrodite, 300/290 B.C. Ht. 29 cm. Room V : 10

13 Head from statue of an athlete, 360/350 B.C. (copy). Ht. of detail 31 cm.
Room V : 3

14 Head of a youth, from a bronze statue. Roman, beginning of Christian era (after a classical model). Ht. 26 cm. Room III : 7

15 Head of a woman, 300/280 B.C. Ht. 30 cm. Room V : 8

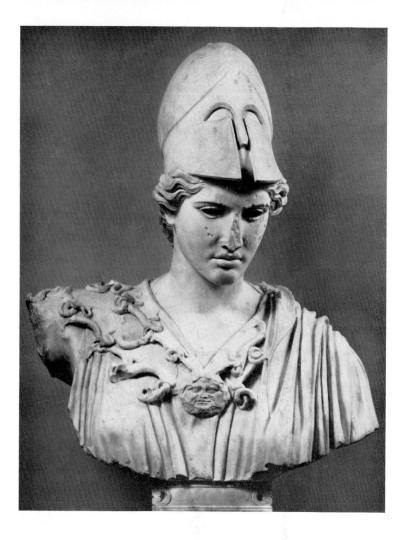

16 Athene, 430/420 B.C. (copy, bust). Ht. 114 cm. Room III : 15

17 Eirene and Ploutos, ca. 370 B.C. (copy). Ht. 206 cm. Room V : 1

18 Relief from a grave lekythos, ca. 370 B.C. Ht. of detail 39 cm. Room IV : 10

19 Grave relief of Mnesarete, ca. 380 B.C. Ht. 166 cm. Room IV : 1

20 Grave relief, lady with her maid, ca. 400 B.C. Ht. 100 cm. Room VI : 4

21 Grave relief, huntsman with hound, ca. 360 B.C. Ht. 120 cm. Room VI : 1

22 Head of Athene from West pediment of temple at Aegina, 505/500 B.C. Ht. of detail 29 cm. Room VII

23 Head of warrior from West pediment of temple at Aegina, 505/500 B.C.
Ht. of detail 28 cm. Room VII : 2

24   Head of Ajax from West pediment of temple at Aegina, 505/500 B.C. Ht. of detail 37 cm. Room VII

25 Head of warrior from East pediment of temple at Aegina, 485/480 B.C.
Ht. 24 cm. Room IX : 3

26 Head of the Trojan King Laomedon, from East pediment of temple at Aegina, 485/480 B.C. Ht. of detail 38 cm. Room IX

27 Head of Herakles from East pediment of temple at Aegina, 485/480 B.C. Ht. of detail 25 cm. Room IX

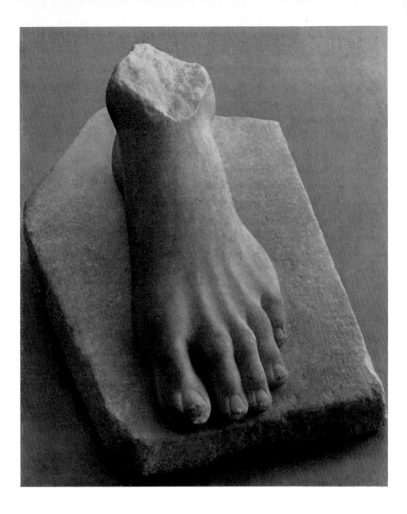

28 Foot of a warrior from West pediment of temple at Aegina, 505/500 B.C. Length 21 cm. Room VII

29 Paris as archer, from West pediment of temple at Aegina, 505/500 B.C.
Ht. 96 cm. Room VII

30   Head of a goddess, 250/200 B.C. (copy). Ht. 45 cm. Room X : 10

31 Head from statue of Alexander, **338/336** B.C. (copy). Ht. of detail 40 cm.
Room X : 1

32 Votive relief with a rustic shrine, ca. 200 B.C. Ht. 62 cm. Room II : 3

33 Wedding of Poseidon and Amphitrite. Relief monument from Rome (detail), ca. 70 B.C. Ht. 80 cm. Room XI : 16

34 Bust of a young man, 40/30 B.C. Ht. 40 cm. Room XI : 6

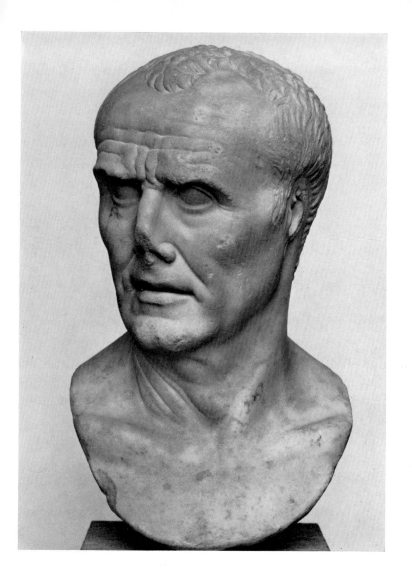

35 Bust of a Roman, so-called ‹Marius›, 50/40 B.C. Ht. 46 cm. Room XI : 13

36 Head of T. Caesernius Statianus (from a statue in armour), ca. 130 A.D.
Ht. 39 cm. Room XI : 29

37 Bust of Augustus (ruled 31 B.C. – 14 A. D.), 40/50 A.D. Ht. 43 cm. Room
XI : 1

38 Bust of a man, 110/120 A.D. Ht. 49 cm. Room XI : 19

39   Bust of a man, 130/140 A.D. Ht. 64 cm. Room XI : 33

40 Septimius Severus (Emperor 193–211), 200/210 A.D. Ht. 82 cm. Room XI : 49

41   Bust of a woman, 240/250 A.D. Ht. 68 cm. Room XI : 53

42   Head of a man, ca. 400 A.D. Ht. 30 cm. Room XI : 64

43 Head of Julia Domna, wife of Septimius Severus, ca. 195 A.D. Ht. 37 cm.
Room XI : 51

44 Head of a man (from a statue), 240 A.D. Ht. 41 cm. Room XI : 55

45 Head of a huntsman, relief from a sarcophagus, 250/260 A.D. Ht. of detail
39 cm. Room XI : 65

46 Boy with the Goose, 250/200 B.C. (copy). Ht. 84 cm. Room XIII : 1